# Everyday Mathematics

## Student Math Journal 1

The University of Chicago
School Mathematics Project

| DATE DUE | |
| --- | --- |
|  |  |
|  |  |
|  |  |
|  |  |
|  |  |
|  |  |
|  |  |
|  |  |
|  |  |
|  |  |
|  |  |
|  |  |
|  |  |

BRODART, CO.                                    Cat. No. 23-221-003

SRA

*A Division of The McGraw·Hill Companies*

*Columbus, Ohio*
*Chicago, Illinois*

## UCSMP Elementary Materials Component
Max Bell, Director

**Authors**
Max Bell
John Bretzlauf
Amy Dillard
Robert Hartfield
Andy Isaacs
James McBride, Director
Kathleen Pitvorec
Peter Saecker
Robert Balfanz*
William Carroll*
Sheila Sconiers*

**Technical Art**
Diana Barrie

*First Edition only*

 This material is based upon work supported by the National Science Foundation under Grant No. ESI-9252984. Any opinions, findings, and conclusions or recommendations expressed in this materia those of the authors and do not necessarily reflect the views of the National Science Foundation.

(

**www.sra4kids.com**

*SRA/McGraw-Hill*

*A Division of The McGraw·Hill Companies*

Send all inquiries to:
SRA/McGraw-Hill
P.O. BOX 812960
Chicago, IL 60681

Printed in the United States of America.

ISBN 1-57039-906-9

5 6 7 8 9 DBH 07 06 05 04 03 02

# Contents

## Unit 1: Naming and Constructing Geometric Figures

A note at the bottom of each journal page indicates when that page is first used. Some pages will be used again during the course of the year.

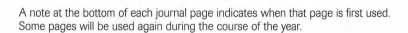

# Unit 2: Using Numbers and Organizing Data

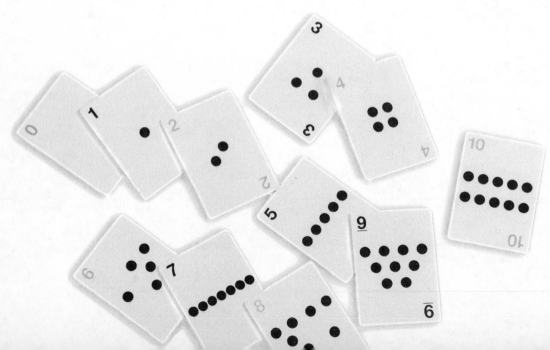

# Unit 3: Multiplication and Division

# Unit 4: Decimals and Their Uses

# Unit 5: Big Numbers, Estimation, and Computation

# Unit 6: Division; Map Reference Frames; Measures of Angles

## Activity Sheets

# Welcome to *Fourth Grade Everyday Mathematics*®

Much of your work in kindergarten through third grade was basic training in mathematics and its uses. You spent quite a bit of time and effort telling and solving number stories and learning arithmetic, including the basic addition and multiplication facts.

*Fourth Grade Everyday Mathematics* builds on this basic training and begins to make the transition to mathematics concepts and ways of using mathematics that are more like what your parents and older siblings may have learned in high school. We believe, along with many other people, that fourth graders today can learn more and do more than was thought to be possible ten or twenty years ago.

Here are some things you will be asked to do in *Fourth Grade Everyday Mathematics:*

- Strengthen and increase your "number sense," "measure sense," and estimation skills.

- Review and extend your skills in the basics of arithmetic—addition, subtraction, multiplication, and division. There isn't much more to learn about the arithmetic of whole numbers, but over the next couple of years you will become comfortable with the many uses of fractions, percents, and decimals.

- Learn about "variables" (letters that stand for numbers) and other topics in algebra that your parents or brothers and sisters may not have learned until they were in high school.

- Develop your geometry skills and concepts further, with more exact definitions and classifications of geometric figures, with constructions and transformations of figures, and with more work on areas of 2-dimensional figures and volumes of 3-dimensional shapes.

- Take a World Tour. Along the way you will consider many kinds of data about various countries and learn about coordinate systems used to locate places on world globes and on flat maps.

- Do many projects involving numerical data.

In fourth grade, you will be asked to do more independent reading and to rely on what you can find out for yourself (often working with partners or in groups) rather than being told everything by your teacher.

The authors hope that you find the activities fun and that you see some of the real beauty in mathematics. And most importantly, they hope you become better and better at using mathematics to sort out and solve interesting problems in your life.

# Using Your *Student Reference Book*

Use your *Student Reference Book* to complete the following:

1. Look up the word **mode** in the Glossary.

   a. Copy the definition. _____

   _____

   b. On which page in the *Student Reference Book* could you find more information

   about the mode of a set of data? _____

2. Read the essay "Comparing Numbers and Amounts."

   a. Solve the Check Your Understanding problems.

   Problem 1: _____          Problem 2: _____

   Problem 3: _____          Problem 4: _____

   b. Check your answers in the Answer Key.

   c. Describe what you did to find the essay.

   _____

   _____

3. Look up the rules for the game *Beat the Calculator*.

   a. On which page did you find the rules? _____

   b. How many players are needed for the game? _____

4. Find the World Tour section. Record two interesting facts you find there.

   a. Fact 1: _____

   I found this information on page _____.

   b. Fact 2: _____

   I found this information on page _____.

Use with Lesson 1.1.

## Math Boxes 1.1

**1.** Add.

   **a.** $32 + 35 = $ _____

   **b.** $38 + 66 = $ _____

SRB
9 10

---

**2.** Add or subtract.

   **a.** $1 + 7 = $ _____

   **b.** $4 + 0 = $ _____

   **c.** $2 + 9 = $ _____

   **d.** $8 - 0 = $ _____

   **e.** $5 - 1 = $ _____

   **f.** $6 - 4 = $ _____

**3.** What numbers come next?

   **a.** 2, 4, 6, 8, _____, _____, _____

   **b.** 50, 45, 40, _____, _____, _____

   **c.** 30, 40, 50, _____, _____, _____

   **d.** 18, 15, 12, _____, _____, _____

---

**4.** Complete.

   **a.** 1 week = _____ days

   **b.** _____ days = 3 weeks

   **c.** 4 weeks 3 days = _____ days

   **d.** _____ weeks = 14 days

   **e.** 24 days = _____ weeks _____ days

**5.** Complete.

   **a.** 2 quarters = _____ dimes

   **b.** 1 dollar and 5 nickels =

      _____ quarters

   **c.** 14 dimes = _____ pennies

   **d.** 8 quarters = _____ dollars

---

# Points, Line Segments, Lines, and Rays

Use a straightedge to draw the following:

1. a. Draw and label line segment TO ($\overline{TO}$).




   b. What is another name for $\overline{TO}$? _____

2. a. Draw and label line IF ($\overleftrightarrow{IF}$). Draw and label point T on it.




   b. What are two other names for $\overleftrightarrow{IF}$? _____

3. a. Draw and label ray ON ($\overrightarrow{ON}$). Draw and label point R on it.




   b. What is another name for $\overrightarrow{ON}$? _____

4. a. Below, draw a line segment from each point
      to each of the other points.

                    M                     N
                    •                     •



              •                                •
              O                                P

   b. How many line segments did you draw? _____

   c. Write a name for each line segment you drew.

   _____

   _____

**1.** Subtract.

   **a.** 86 − 21 = _____

   **b.** 93 − 28 = _____

SRB
11-14

---

**2.** Add or subtract.

   **a.** 3 + 3 = _____

   **b.** _____ = 4 + 6

   **c.** _____ = 5 + 9

   **d.** 8 − 8 = _____

   **e.** 7 − 3 = _____

   **f.** _____ = 9 − 4

---

**3.** Draw and label line *QR*.
Draw point *S* on it.

What are two other names for line *QR*?

_____

_____

SRB
77

---

**4.** It takes Pablo about 50 minutes to get ready for school. If the bus comes at 8:00 A.M., about what time should he get up?

_____ A.M.

---

**5.** Three of the names do not belong in this box. Cross them out. Write the name of the number on the box tag.

| |
|---|
| 25 − 13 |
| 20 − 7 |
| 6 × 2 |
| 4 × 3 |
| 40 − 23 |
| 7 × 3 |

SRB
131

## Date                Time

# Angles

1. Which angle below is bigger, ∠ABC or ∠DEF? _____

2. Draw ∠BAC. What is another name for ∠BAC? _____

3. What is the vertex of ∠BAC? Point _____

4. Feng said the name of this angle is ∠SRT. Is he right? Explain.

_____

_____

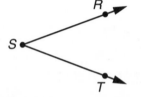

Use the points shown on the grid below to draw angles.

5. Draw ∠AED. Draw $\overrightarrow{ED}$ and $\overrightarrow{EA}$ through points D and A.

   a. What is the vertex of the angle?                         Point _____

   b. What is another name for ∠AED?                     ∠_____

6. Draw a right angle whose vertex is point C.       My angle is called ∠_____.

7. Draw an angle that is smaller than a right angle.     My angle is called ∠_____.

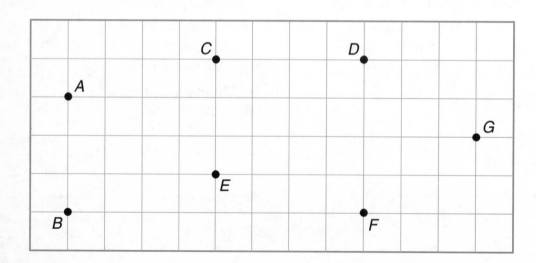

Use with Lesson 1.3.

## Math Boxes 1.3

**1.** Add.

    **a.** 63 + 12 = _____

    **b.** 56 + 97 = _____

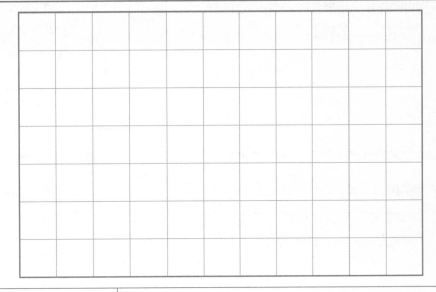

**2.** Add or subtract.

    **a.** 2 + 5 = _____

    **b.** 6 + 8 = _____

    **c.** 9 + 3 = _____

    **d.** _____ = 12 − 5

    **e.** _____ = 15 − 9

    **f.** _____ = 11 − 7

**3.** What numbers come next?

    **a.** 4, 8, 12, 16, _____, _____, _____

    **b.** 33, 30, 27, _____, _____, _____

    **c.** 20, 35, 50, _____, _____, _____

    **d.** 37, 31, 25, _____, _____, _____

**4.** Complete.

    **a.** 2 weeks = _____ days

    **b.** 11 weeks = _____ days

    **c.** 5 weeks 4 days = _____ days

    **d.** 21 days = _____ weeks

    **e.** 30 days = _____ weeks _____ days

**5.** Complete.

    **a.** 4 quarters = _____ dimes

    **b.** 2 dollars and 10 nickels =

        _____ quarters

    **c.** 9 dimes = _____ pennies

    **d.** 30 dimes = _____ dollars

# Parallelograms

1. Circle the pairs of line segments below that are parallel. Check your answers by extending each pair of segments to see if the two segments in the pair meet.

   a. ——————
                    b.          c.                    d.

Use your Geometry Template or straightedge to draw the following quadrangles:

2. Draw a quadrangle that has two pairs of parallel sides.

3. Draw a quadrangle that has only one pair of parallel sides.

   This is called a _____.      This is called a _____.

4. A **parallelogram** is a quadrangle that has two pairs of parallel sides. Which of the following quadrangles are parallelograms?

   a. squares        b. rectangles        c. rhombuses        d. trapezoids

5. A **rhombus** is a parallelogram in which all sides are the same length. Which of the following quadrangles are always rhombuses?

   a. squares        b. rectangles        c. trapezoids

6. A **rectangle** is a parallelogram that has all right angles. Which of the following are rectangles? Write **always, sometimes,** or **never** to complete each sentence.

   a. **Squares** are _____ rectangles.

   b. **Rhombuses** are _____ rectangles.

   c. **Trapezoids** are _____ rectangles.

7. Is a kite a parallelogram? _____ Explain below.

   _____

   _____

Use with Lesson 1.4.

# Math Boxes 1.4

**1.** Subtract.

    **a.** 76 − 41 = _____

    **b.** 52 − 38 = _____

**2.** Add or subtract.

    **a.** 5 + 6 = _____

    **b.** _____ = 7 + 8

    **c.** _____ = 3 + 2

    **d.** 10 − 7 = _____

    **e.** 13 − 8 = _____

    **f.** _____ = 14 − 6

**3.** Draw and label line *AB*.
Draw point *C* on it.

What are two other names for line *AB*?

_____

_____

**4.** The bus arrives at 3:20 P.M. It is now
2:57 P.M. The bus will arrive in how
many minutes?

_____ minutes

**5.** Three of the names
do not belong in this
box. Cross them
out. Write the name
of the number on
the box tag.

| |
|---|
| 25 + 25 |
| 10 + 35 |
| 101 − 51 |
| 80 − 40 |
| 41 + 9 |
| 4 × 10 |

# What Is a Polygon?

These are polygons.

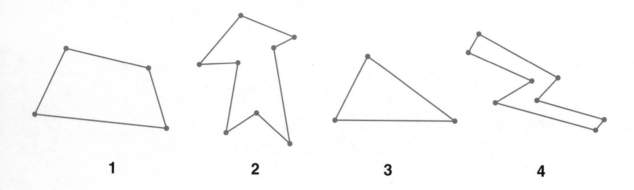

1  2  3  4

These are not polygons.

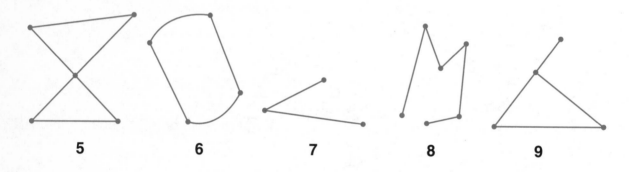

5  6  7  8  9

If you had to explain what a polygon is, what would you say?

_____

_____

_____

_____

_____

_____

Use with Lesson 1.5.

Date

# Math Boxes 1.5

1. Put these numbers in order from smallest to largest.

   10,005          5,100

   51,000          10,500

   _____

   _____

   _____

   _____

2. Draw ∠ART. What is another name for

   ∠ART ? _____

   •T

   •
   A

   •
   R

3. Add or subtract.

   a. 6 + 3 = _____

   b. 1 + 4 = _____

   c. _____ = 9 + 9

   d. _____ = 10 − 8

   e. 13 − 7 = _____

   f. 16 − 9 = _____

4. Draw and label line segment AB.

5. Name as many rays as you can in the figure below.

   M          N          O

   Write their names.

   _____

   _____

6. Draw a quadrangle with 2 pairs of parallel sides.

   What kind of quadrangle is this?

   _____

# An Inscribed Square

Follow the directions below to make a square.

**Step 1** Use your compass to draw a circle on a sheet of paper. The circle should be small enough to fit on the next page. Cut out the circle.

**Step 2** With your pencil, make a dot in the center of the circle, where the hole is, on both the front and the back.

**Step 3** Fold the circle in half. Make sure that the edges match and that the fold line passes through the center.

**Step 4** Fold the folded circle in half again so that the edges match.

**Step 5** Unfold your circle. The folds should pass through the center of the circle and form four right angles.

**Step 6** Connect the endpoints of the folds with a straightedge to make a square. Cut out the square.

Use with Lesson 1.6.

# An Inscribed Square (cont.)

Now use your compass to find out whether the four sides of your square are all about the same length. If they are, paste or tape the square in the space below. If not, follow the directions on page 12 again. Paste or tape your second square in the space below.

# Math Boxes 1.6

**1.** In the numeral 42,018, the 2 stands for 2,000.

   **a.** The 1 stands for _____.

   **b.** The 8 stands for _____.

   **c.** The 4 stands for _____.

SRB
4

**2.** Which of the shape(s) below are **not** polygons? _____

   A          B          C

SRB
82

**3.** Add or subtract.

   **a.** $6 + 7 =$ _____

   **b.** $8 + 8 =$ _____

   **c.** _____ $= 9 + 4$

   **d.** _____ $= 12 - 9$

   **e.** $14 - 7 =$ _____

   **f.** $13 - 5 =$ _____

**4.** Draw a quadrangle that does not have any right angles.

SRB
86

**5.** Circle the convex polygons.

SRB
83

**6.** Draw and label ray *HA*.
Draw point *T* on it.

What is another name for ray *HA*?

_____

SRB
77

                                  Use with Lesson 1.6.

# Circle Constructions

Do each of the following 3 constructions on a separate sheet of paper. Try and try again until you are satisfied with your work. Then cut out your 3 best constructions and paste them in your journal.

1. Use your compass to draw a picture of a circular dartboard. Paste your best work in the space below.

The circles in your picture are called **concentric circles.**

# Circle Constructions (cont.)

**2. a.** Make a dot near the center of your paper. Use your compass to draw a circle with that dot as its center.

**b.** *Without changing the opening of your compass,* draw a second circle that passes through the center of the first circle. Mark the center of the second circle.

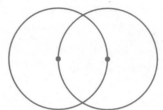

**c.** *Without changing the opening of your compass,* draw a third circle that passes through the center of each of the first two circles.

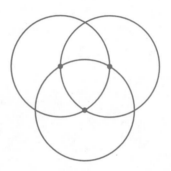

Try and try again until you are satisfied with your work. Then cut out your circle design and paste it in the space below.

Use with Lesson 1.7.

# Circle Constructions (cont.)

## Challenge

3. Try to draw this design with your compass. Work on separate sheets of paper until you are satisfied with your work. Color your best design. Then cut it out and paste it in the space below.

   *Hint:* Start by making the 3-circle design on page 16. Then add more circles to it.

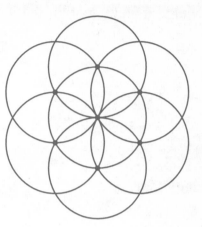

# Polygon Checklist

Place a check mark next to all of the statements that are true about each figure.
Write an additional true statement for that figure.

**1.**

_____ 1 pair of parallel sides

_____ at least 1 right angle

_____ quadrangle

_____ polygon

_____ concave

_____ parallelogram

✓ _____

**2.**

_____ 4 sides of equal length

_____ kite

_____ square

_____ parallelogram

_____ convex

_____ opposite sides parallel

✓ _____

**3.**

_____ all sides of equal length

_____ all angles of equal measure

_____ one right angle

_____ polygon

_____ equilateral triangle

_____ 1 pair of parallel sides

✓ _____

**4.**

_____ regular polygon

_____ all sides of equal length

_____ all angles of equal measure

_____ pentagon

_____ octagon

_____ all angles smaller than right angles

✓ _____

## Math Boxes 1.7

**1.** Put these numbers in order from smallest to largest.

32,000          3,200

23,000          2,300

_____

_____

_____

_____

**2.** Draw ∠*TIF*. What is the vertex of ∠*TIF*? _____

*F* •

• *T*

*I* •

**3.** Add or subtract.

a. $8 + 3 =$ _____

b. $6 + 6 =$ _____

c. _____ $= 5 + 7$

d. _____ $= 13 - 9$

e. _____ $= 11 - 4$

f. $10 - 5 =$ _____

**4.** Draw and label line segment *GP*.

**5.** Name as many rays as you can in the figure below.

L   M          N   O   P

Write their names.

_____

_____

**6.** Draw a quadrangle with 1 pair of parallel sides.

What kind of quadrangle is this?

_____

# Copying a Line Segment

Steps 1–4 below show you how to copy a line segment.

**Step 1** You are given line segment *AB* to copy.

**Step 2** Draw a line segment longer than line segment *AB*. Label one of its endpoints *C*.

**Step 3** Open your compass so that the anchor is on one endpoint of line segment *AB* and the pencil point is on the other endpoint.

**Step 4** *Without changing the compass opening,* place the anchor on point *C* on your second line segment. Make a mark that crosses this line segment. Label the point where the mark crosses the line segment with the letter *D*.

Line segment *CD* should be about the same length as line segment *AB*.

Use a compass and straightedge to copy the line segments shown below.

**1.**   E ———————————————————— F

**2.**   M ———————————————————— N

**3.**   R ———————————————————————————————————— T

# Constructing a Regular, Inscribed Hexagon

Hexagons are seen in the natural world and in things that people make and use. For example, honeycombs are built with many hexagonal shapes, and snowflakes suggest the shape of a hexagon.

Soccer balls are made up of regular hexagons and regular pentagons.

For many centuries, wonderful tile designs have been created all over the world. Some of the best tile designs are from Islamic art. The designs often start with hexagons, which fit together without gaps or overlaps. As these pictures show, tile designs can be developed in many ways from a pattern that uses hexagons.

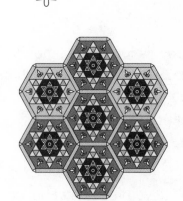

Many quilt and fabric designs come from dividing regular hexagons into triangles or rhombuses. You may have made designs like these with pattern blocks. Coloring a design can be fun, and it often makes the design more interesting.

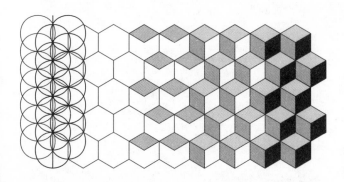

# Constructing a Regular, Inscribed Hexagon (cont.)

Follow each step below. Draw on a separate sheet of paper. Repeat these steps several times. Tape or paste your best work onto the bottom of this page.

**Step 1** Draw a circle. (Keep the same compass opening for Steps 2 and 3.) Draw a dot on the circle. Place the anchor of your compass on the dot and draw a mark on the circle.

**Step 2** Place the anchor of your compass on the mark you just made and draw another mark on the circle.

**Step 3** Do this four more times to divide the circle into 6 equal parts. The 6th mark should be on the dot you started with or very close to it.

**Step 4** With your straightedge, connect the 6 marks on the circle to form a regular hexagon. Use your compass to check that the sides of the hexagon are all about the same length.

                                Use with Lesson 1.8.

# More Constructions

Construct a regular hexagon on a separate sheet of paper. Then divide the hexagon into 6 equilateral triangles.

Try this several times until you are satisfied with your work. Tape or paste your best work in the space below.

1. In the numeral 30,516,

   a. the 3 stands for _____.

   b. the 5 stands for _____.

   c. the 1 stands for _____.

   d. the 6 stands for _____.

2. Which of the shape(s) below are

   polygons? _____

   A           B           C

3. Add or subtract.

   a. $6 + 9 =$ _____

   b. _____ $= 7 + 4$

   c. _____ $= 8 + 9$

   d. $14 - 9 =$ _____

   e. _____ $= 12 - 6$

   f. _____ $= 15 - 7$

4. Draw a quadrangle that has two pairs of parallel sides and no right angles.

   What kind of quadrangle is this?

   _____

5. Circle the concave (nonconvex) polygons.

6. Draw and label ray *CA*.
   Draw point *R* on it.

   What is another name for ray *CA*?

   _____

Use with Lesson 1.8.

# Time to Reflect

1. Write 2 or 3 interesting things you have learned about geometry.

_____

_____

_____

_____

_____

_____

2. What do you think the difference is between *drawing* a geometric figure and *constructing* a geometric figure?

_____

_____

_____

_____

_____

_____

_____

3. What was the hardest part of this unit for you?

_____

_____

_____

_____

_____

_____

_____

# Math Boxes 1.9

**1.** Add.

    **a.**       64       **b.**       48
          + 32          + 96

**2.** Subtract.

    **a.**       78       **b.**       81
          − 42          − 36

**3.** Put these numbers in order from smallest to largest.

46,000       40,600

4,600         4,006

_____

_____

_____

_____

**4.** In the numeral 78,965,

    **a.** the 8 stands for _____.

    **b.** the 6 stands for _____.

    **c.** the 7 stands for _____.

    **d.** the 9 stands for _____.

**5.** Use the following list of numbers to answer the questions:

12, 3, 15, 6, 12, 14, 6, 5, 9, 12

    **a.** Which number is the smallest? _____

    **b.** Which number is the largest? _____

    **c.** What is the difference between the smallest and largest numbers? _____

    **d.** Which number appears most often? _____

Use with Lesson 1.9.

# A Visit to Washington, D.C.

Refer to pages 211 and 212 in your *Student Reference Book.*

1.  About how many people tour the White House every year?
    Check the best answer.

    ____ between 100 thousand and 1 million      ____ between 1 million and 10 million

    ____ between 10 million and 100 million      ____ between 100 million and 1 billion

2.  About how many people ride the Washington Metrorail on an average weekday?
    Check the best answer.

    ____ between 100 thousand and 1 million      ____ between 1 million and 10 million

    ____ between 10 million and 100 million      ____ between 100 million and 1 billion

3.  The Library of Congress adds about _____ items each day. About how many days

    does it take to add 50,000 items to the Library of Congress? _____

4.  Write the year that each event happened. Then draw a dot for each event
    on the timeline below. Label the dot with the correct letter and date.

    A  The year the Metrorail opened ____*1976*____

    B  The year of the flight of the *Flyer* _____

    C  The year the Washington Monument was completed _____

    D  The year the Lincoln Memorial was dedicated _____

    E  The year of the first nonstop flight across the Atlantic _____

    F  The year the Jefferson Memorial was dedicated _____

    G  The year of the first landing on the moon _____

# Math Boxes 2.1

---

**1.** Complete the division facts.

    **a.** 28 ÷ 4 = _____

    **b.** 27 ÷ _____ = 9

    **c.** 42 ÷ _____ = 6

    **d.** 24 ÷ _____ = 6

    **e.** 36 ÷ 6 = _____

    **f.** 90 ÷ 9 = _____

**2.** A giant tortoise can live about 150 years. An elephant can live about 78 years. About how much longer can a giant tortoise live than an elephant?

    About _____ years

SRB
132  152

---

**3.** What is the value of the digit 7 in the numerals below?

    **a.** 474          _____

    **b.** 70,158     _____

    **c.** 187,943    _____

    **d.** 2,731,008  _____

SRB
4

**4.** Add.

    **a.** 3 + 5 = _____

    **b.** 30 + 50 = _____

    **c.** 300 + 500 = _____

    **d.** _____ = 9 + 7

    **e.** _____ = 90 + 70

    **f.** _____ = 900 + 700

---

**5.** Solve the riddle.

I am a 2-dimensional figure.
I have two pairs of parallel sides.
All my angles have the same measure.
All my sides are the same length.

What am I? _____

SRB
86

**6.** Circle the pair of concentric circles.

---

# Name-Collection Boxes

Write 5 names in each box below. Use as many different kinds of numbers and operations as you can. Draw an asterisk (*) next to the name you find most interesting.

**1.**

| 24 |
| --- |
| 8 × 3 |
| 36 − 12 |
|  |
|  |
|  |

**2.**

| 100 |
| --- |
|  |
|  |
|  |
|  |
|  |

**3.**

| 50 |
| --- |
|  |
|  |
|  |
|  |
|  |

**4.**

| 16 |
| --- |
|  |
|  |
|  |
|  |
|  |

Write in your own numbers and fill in the boxes.

**5.**

**6.**

# Math Boxes 2.2

---

**1.** A square number is the product of a number multiplied by itself. For example, 9 is a square number since 3 ∗ 3 = 9. Circle the numbers below that are square numbers.

| | | |
|---|---|---|
| 49 | 15 | 12 |
| 36 | 25 | 16 |

*SRB* 138

**2.** Write the largest number you can make with the digits 3, 0, 3, 8, and 0.

_____

---

**3.** Add.

a.     27  
    + 139

b.     460  
    + 394

 *SRB* 9  10

**4.** Draw a convex pentagon.

 *SRB* 83

---

**5. a.** Without measuring, estimate the length of this line segment to the nearest inch.

_____

About _____ in.

**b.** Measure the line segment to the nearest inch.

About _____ in.

 *SRB* 108

Use with Lesson 2.2.

Date _____    Time _____

# Place-Value Chart

| Number | Hundred-Millions | Ten-Millions | Millions | Hundred-Thousands | Ten-Thousands | Thousands | Hundreds | Tens | Ones |
|---|---|---|---|---|---|---|---|---|---|
| | 100M | 10M | M | 100K | 10K | K | H | T | O |
| | | | | | | | | | |
| | | | | | | | | | |
| | | | | | | | | | |
| | | | | | | | | | |
| | | | | | | | | | |
| | | | | | | | | | |
| | | | | | | | | | |

# Taking Apart, Putting Together

Complete.

1. In 574,

   5 is worth _____500_____

   7 is worth _____

   4 is worth _____

2. In 9,027,

   9 is worth _____

   0 is worth _____

   2 is worth _____

   7 is worth _____

3. In 280,743,

   8 is worth _____

   2 is worth _____

   4 is worth _____

4. In 56,010,837,

   6 is worth _____

   1 is worth _____

   5 is worth _____

5. In 705,622,463,

   5 is worth _____

   4 is worth _____

   7 is worth _____

6. In 123,456,789,

   4 is worth _____

   9 is worth _____

   2 is worth _____

Add.

7.
```
    900
     70
 +    5
```

8.
```
   30,000
    7,000
       50
 +      2
```

9.
```
   50,000,000
    9,000,000
       60,000
        2,000
          800
 +         50
```

10.
```
   300,000,000
     9,000,000
       200,000
        70,000
            30
 +           1
```

Use with Lesson 2.3.

# Math Boxes 2.3

**1.** Complete the division facts.

    **a.** $63 \div 9 =$ _____

    **b.** $36 \div$ _____ $= 9$

    **c.** $48 \div$ _____ $= 6$

    **d.** $60 \div$ _____ $= 6$

    **e.** $30 \div 6 =$ _____

    **f.** $81 \div 9 =$ _____

**2.** A sailfish can swim at a speed of 110 kilometers per hour. A tiger shark can swim at a speed of 53 kilometers per hour. How much faster can a sailfish swim than a tiger shark?

    _____ kilometers per hour

**3.** What is the value of the digit 8 in the numerals below?

    **a.** 584      _____

    **b.** 38,067      _____

    **c.** 49,841      _____

    **d.** 820,731      _____

**4.** Add.

    **a.** $4 + 5 =$ _____

    **b.** $40 + 50 =$ _____

    **c.** $400 + 500 =$ _____

    **d.** _____ $= 5 + 8$

    **e.** _____ $= 50 + 80$

    **f.** _____ $= 500 + 800$

**5.** Solve the riddle.

I am a 2-dimensional figure.
I have two pairs of parallel sides.
None of my angles is a right angle.
All my sides are the same length.

What am I? _____

**6.** Use your compass to draw a pair of concentric circles.

# Math Boxes 2.4

---

**1.** Circle the numbers below that are square numbers.

34          4          64

81          88          100

---

**2.** Write the largest number you can make with the digits 5, 2, 3, 0, 6, 0, and 4.

_____

---

**3.** Add.

a.      145
      + 36

b.      290
      + 136

---

**4.** Draw a concave pentagon.

---

**5. a.** Without measuring, estimate the length of this line segment to the nearest inch.

_____

About _____ in.

**b.** Measure the line segment to the nearest inch.

About _____ in.

---

# Counting Raisins

1. Use your $\frac{1}{2}$-ounce box of raisins. Complete each step when the teacher tells you. Stop after you complete each step.

   a. Don't open your box yet. **Guess** about how many raisins are in the box.

   About _____ raisins

   b. Open the box. Count the number of raisins in the top layer. Then **estimate** the total number of raisins in the box.

   About _____ raisins

   c. Now **count** the raisins in the box.

   How many? _____ raisins

3. Find the following **landmarks** for the class data.

   a. What is the **maximum,** or largest, number of raisins found? _____

   b. What is the **minimum,** or smallest, number of raisins found? _____

   c. What is the **range**? (Subtract the minimum from the maximum.) _____

   d. What is the **mode,** or most frequent number of raisins found? _____

2. Make a tally chart of the class data.

| Number of Raisins | Number of Boxes |
|---|---|
|  |  |
|  |  |
|  |  |
|  |  |
|  |  |
|  |  |
|  |  |
|  |  |
|  |  |
|  |  |
|  |  |
|  |  |
|  |  |

## Math Boxes 2.5

**1.** Complete the multiplication facts.

    **a.** $5 * 7 =$ _____

    **b.** $3 *$ _____ $= 18$

    **c.** $7 *$ _____ $= 56$

    **d.** $9 *$ _____ $= 45$

    **e.** $8 * 4 =$ _____

    **f.** $8 * 9 =$ _____

**2.** Name the two pairs of parallel sides in parallelogram *HIJK*.

_____ and _____

_____ and _____

SRB
80

**3.** A number has

6 in the hundreds place,
1 in the millions place,
2 in the tens place,
8 in the hundred-thousands place,
5 in the ones place,
3 in the thousands place, and
4 in the ten-thousands place.

Write the number.

____ , ____ ____ ____ , ____ ____ ____

SRB
4

**4.** Write 5 names for 34.

_____

_____

_____

_____

_____

SRB
131

**5. a.** Without measuring, estimate the length of this line segment to the nearest centimeter.

_____

    About _____ cm

    **b.** Measure the line segment to the nearest centimeter.

    About _____ cm

SRB
108

Use with Lesson 2.5.

Date _____                    Time _____

# Family Size

Follow your teacher's directions and complete each step.

1. How many people are in your family? _____
   Write the number on a stick-on note.

2. Make a line plot of the family-size data for the class.
   Use **X**s in place of stick-on notes.

**Class Data on Family Size**

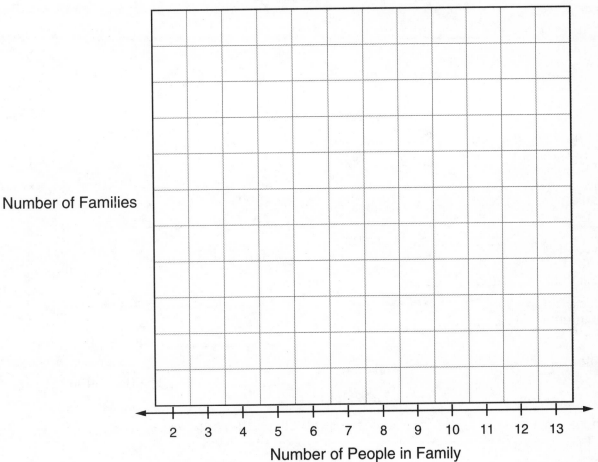

Number of Families

Number of People in Family

3. Find the following landmarks for the class data:

   a. What is the **maximum** (largest) number of people in a family? _____

   b. What is the **minimum** (smallest) number of people in a family? _____

   c. What is the **range**? (Subtract the minimum from the maximum.) _____

   d. What is the **mode** (most frequent family size)? _____

4. What is the **median** family size for the class? _____ people

# Math Boxes 2.6

---

**1.** Tell whether each number sentence is true or false.

    **a.** $14 + 7 = 22$ _____

    **b.** $45 - 12 = 33$ _____

    **c.** $27 = 40 - 13$ _____

    **d.** $36 = 15 + 15$ _____

**2.** A royal python can be 35 feet long. An anaconda can be 28 feet long. What would be their combined length, end-to-end?

    _____ feet

---

**3.** Find the following landmarks for this set of numbers: 3, 45, 15, 13, 3, 7, 19.

    **a.** median _____

    **b.** mode _____

    **c.** maximum _____

    **d.** minimum _____

    **e.** range _____

**4.** Add.

    **a.** $2 + 7 =$ _____

    **b.** $20 + 70 =$ _____

    **c.** $200 + 700 =$ _____

    **d.** _____ $= 8 + 4$

    **e.** _____ $= 80 + 40$

    **f.** _____ $= 800 + 400$

---

**5.** Subtract.

    **a.** $\begin{array}{r} 147 \\ -\ 56 \\ \hline \end{array}$      **b.** $\begin{array}{r} 531 \\ -\ 246 \\ \hline \end{array}$

**6.** Write 4,007,392 in words.

_____

_____

_____

_____

_____

Use with Lesson 2.6.

# Partial-Sums Addition

Solve Problems 1–3 using the partial-sums method. Solve Problems 4–6 using any method you choose. Show your work.

**1.** 76 + 38 = _____

**2.** 166 + 28 = _____

**3.** _____ = 647 + 936

**4.** _____ = 6,236 + 645

**5.** _____ = 1,672 + 3,221

**6.** 17,854 + 24,550 = _____

# Column Addition

Solve Problems 1–3 using the column-addition method. Solve Problems 4–6 using any method you choose. Show your work.

**1.** 94 + 47 = _____

**2.** 549 + 33 = _____

**3.** _____ = 385 + 726

**4.** _____ = 9,046 + 946

**5.** _____ = 2,538 + 4,179

**6.** 24,614 + 73,058 = _____

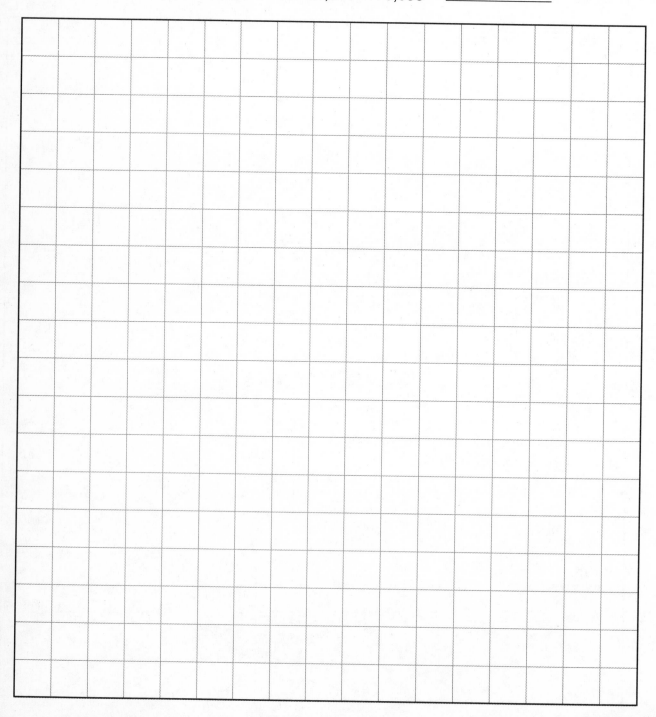

**Use with Lesson 2.7.**

Date _____                    Time _____

# Math Boxes 2.7

1. Complete the multiplication facts.

   a. 5 * 8 = _____

   b. 2 * _____ = 16

   c. 7 * _____ = 21

   d. 9 * _____ = 54

   e. 8 * 3 = _____

   f. 9 * 8 = _____

2. Draw a parallelogram. Label the vertices so that side *AB* is parallel to side *CD*.

3. A number has

   3 in the millions place,
   1 in the ones place,
   8 in the thousands place,
   9 in the ten-thousands place,
   0 in the tens place,
   6 in the hundred-thousands place, and
   5 in the hundreds place.

   Write the number.

   ____, ____ ____ ____, ____ ____ ____

4. Write 5 names for 100.

   _____

   _____

   _____

   _____

   _____

5. a. Without measuring, estimate the length of this line segment to the nearest centimeter.

   _____

   About _____ cm

   b. Measure the line segment to the nearest centimeter.

   About _____ cm

# Head Sizes

Ms. Woods owns a clothing store. She is trying to decide how many children's hats to stock in each possible size. Should she stock the same number of hats in each size? Or should she stock more hats in the more popular sizes?

Help Ms. Woods decide. Pretend that she has asked each class in your school to collect and organize data about students' head sizes. She plans to combine the data for all the classes and then use the data to figure out how many hats of each size to stock.

As a class, collect and organize data about one another's head sizes.

1. Ask your partner to help you measure the distance around your head.

   • Wrap the tape measure once around your head.

   • See where the tape touches the end tip of the tape measure.

   • Read the mark where the tape touches the end tip.

   • Read this length to the nearest $\frac{1}{2}$ centimeter.

   Record your head size.     About _____ cm

2. What is the median head size for the class?     About _____ cm

## What's Your Hat Size?

Men's and women's hats are sized in different ways. The size of a woman's hat—22, for example—is approximately the distance around the head in inches.

To understand a man's hat size—$6\frac{7}{8}$, for example— imagine taking the sweatband inside the hat and forming it into a circle. The size is the diameter of the circle to the nearest $\frac{1}{8}$ inch.

This system began centuries ago, when new hats were round. Men used a device called a hat screw to force their hats into a more comfortable oval shape.

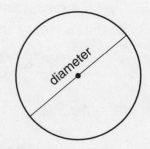

Use with Lesson 2.8.

# Head Sizes (cont.)

3. Make a bar graph of the head-size data for the class.

title

label

label

# Addition of Multidigit Numbers

Use your favorite method to solve the problems.

**1.** 78 + 495 = _____

**2.** _____ = 234 + 681

**3.** 907 + 388 = _____

**4.** 6,891 + 736 = _____

**5.** _____ = 3,801 + 9,777

**6.** _____ = 23,408 + 67,993

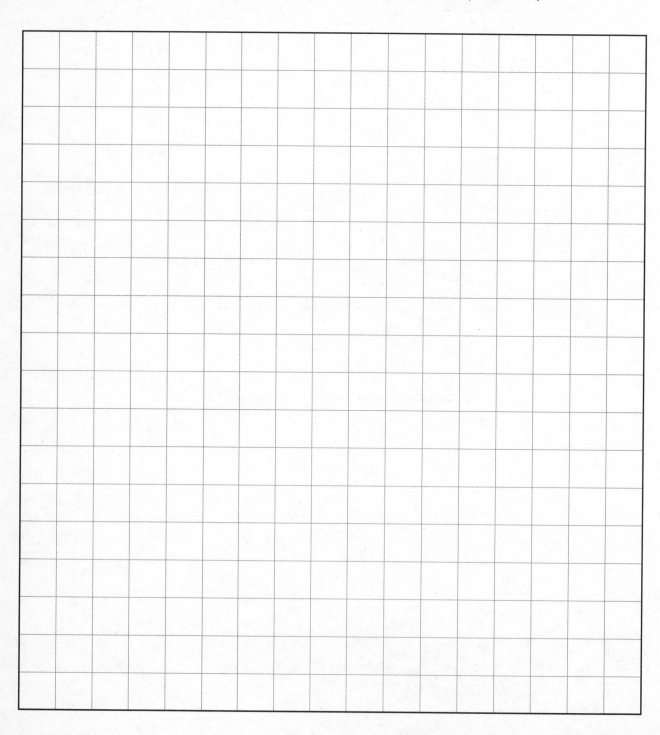

Use with Lesson 2.8.

# Math Boxes 2.8

**1.** Tell whether each number sentence is true or false.

a. $18 + 9 = 37$ _____

b. $29 = 17 + 12$ _____

c. $17 = 40 - 24$ _____

d. $42 - 15 = 27$ _____

**2.** An ostrich can weigh about 345 pounds. An emu can weigh about 88 pounds. How much do they weigh altogether?

_____ pounds

**3.** Find the following landmarks for this set of numbers: 12, 16, 23, 15, 16, 19, 18.

a. median _____

b. mode _____

c. maximum _____

d. minimum _____

e. range _____

**4.** Add.

a. $2 + 4 =$ _____

b. $20 + 40 =$ _____

c. $200 + 400 =$ _____

d. _____ $= 8 + 6$

e. _____ $= 80 + 60$

f. _____ $= 800 + 600$

**5.** Subtract.

a.  $\begin{array}{r} 231 \\ -\ 84 \\ \hline \end{array}$     b.  $\begin{array}{r} 603 \\ -\ 466 \\ \hline \end{array}$

**6.** Write 8,042,176 in words.

_____

_____

_____

_____

_____

# Trade-First Subtraction

Solve Problems 1–3 using the trade-first method. Solve Problems 4–6 using
any method you choose. Show your work.

**1.** 58 − 32 = _____

**2.** 73 − 37 = _____

**3.** _____ = 652 − 379

**4.** _____ = 900 − 461

**5.** _____ = 2,936 − 1,652

**6.** 2,468 − 789 = _____

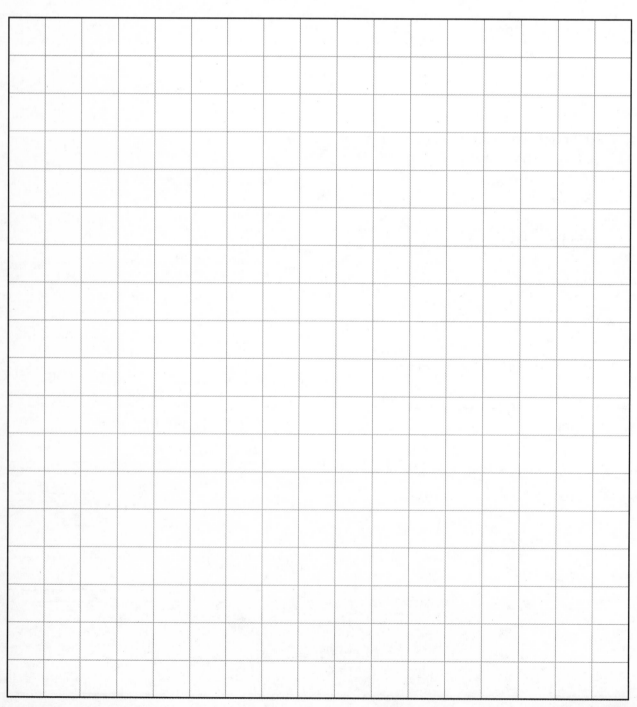

Use with Lesson 2.9.

# Partial-Differences Subtraction

Solve Problems 1–3 using the partial-differences method. Solve Problems 4–6 using any method you choose. Show your work.

1. $86 - 34 =$ _____

2. $61 - 26 =$ _____

3. _____ $= 942 - 485$

4. _____ $= 400 - 271$

5. _____ $= 7,584 - 2,806$

6. $1,681 - 893 =$ _____

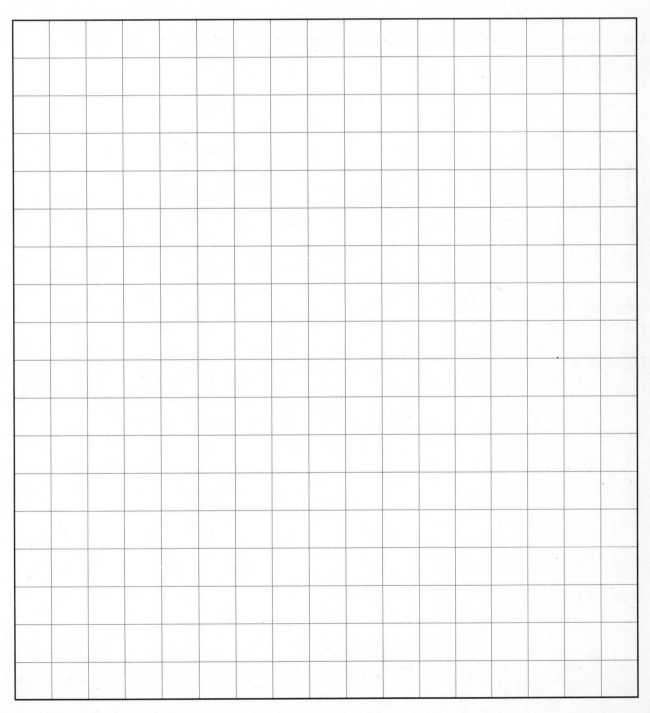

# Subtraction by Counting Up

Solve the problems in your head. Use the counting-up strategy.

*Example*

50 − 26 = ?

Think:   26 + **4** = 30

         30 + **20** = 50

         4 + 20 = 24

So,      50 − 26 = 24

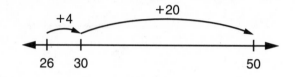

1. 80 − 37 = _____

2. 70 − 29 = _____

3. _____ = 130 − 84

4. _____ = 120 − 45

5. 87 − 20 = _____

6. 63 − 30 = _____

7. _____ = 146 − 90

8. _____ = 224 − 150

9. _____ = 33 − 17

10. 82 − 46 = _____

11. 66 − 37 = _____

12. _____ = 75 − 28

13. _____ = 131 − 86

14. 122 − 58 = _____

**Use with Lesson 2.9.**

# Math Boxes 2.9

---

**1.** Complete the multiplication facts.

   **a.** 5 ∗ 4 = _____

   **b.** 7 ∗ _____ = 63

   **c.** 4 ∗ _____ = 24

   **d.** 6 ∗ _____ = 48

   **e.** 9 ∗ 3 = _____

   **f.** 5 ∗ 6 = _____

**2.** Draw a shape that has no parallel sides.

---

**3.** A number has

   6 in the tens place,
   9 in the millions place,
   4 in the thousands place,
   3 in the ten-thousands place,
   2 in the hundred-thousands place,
   0 in the ones place, and
   8 in the hundreds place.

   Write the number.

   _____ , _____ _____ _____ , _____ _____ _____

**4.** Write 5 names for 1,000.

   _____

   _____

   _____

   _____

   _____

---

**5. a.** Without measuring, estimate the length of this line segment
     to the nearest centimeter.

     _____

     About _____ cm

  **b.** Measure the line segment to the nearest centimeter.

     About _____ cm

---

## Time to Reflect

1. As you discovered the many uses of numbers, did any of the uses surprise you? Why? Why not?

_____

_____

_____

_____

2. When you are filling in a name-collection box, do you find that you tend to use one operation more than any other? How could you break this habit? If you do not have this habit, what advice would you give a classmate to help him or her think creatively about different names for numbers?

_____

_____

_____

_____

3. What is the hardest part of adding or subtracting multidigit numbers? What did you do to overcome these difficulties?

_____

_____

_____

_____

Use with Lesson 2.10.

# Math Boxes 2.10

---

**1.** Complete the division facts.

    **a.** $35 \div 5 =$ _____

    **b.** $56 \div$ _____ $= 8$

    **c.** $32 \div$ _____ $= 4$

    **d.** $24 \div$ _____ $= 6$

    **e.** $72 \div 8 =$ _____

    **f.** $40 \div 5 =$ _____

**2.** Complete the multiplication facts.

    **a.** $4 * 7 =$ _____

    **b.** $3 *$ _____ $= 15$

    **c.** $7 *$ _____ $= 42$

    **d.** $9 *$ _____ $= 36$

    **e.** $6 * 0 =$ _____

    **f.** $1 * 9 =$ _____

---

**3.** Complete the square facts.

    **a.** $64 \div 8 =$ _____

    **b.** $49 \div 7 =$ _____

    **c.** $4 * 4 =$ _____

    **d.** $3 * 3 =$ _____

    **e.** $25 \div 5 =$ _____

**4.** Tell whether each number sentence is true or false.

    **a.** $46 + 12 = 53$    _____

    **b.** $36 = 22 + 14$    _____

    **c.** $13 = 84 - 71$    _____

    **d.** $52 - 20 = 34$    _____

---

**5.** A grizzly bear can weigh 786 pounds. An American black bear can weigh 227 pounds. What is their combined weight?

_____ pounds

**6.** On the average, India produces about 851 movies per year. The United States produces about 569 movies. On the average, how many fewer movies per year does the United States produce than India?

_____

---

# Multiplication/Division Facts Table

| *,/ | 1 | 2 | 3 | 4 | 5 | 6 | 7 | 8 | 9 | 10 |
|---|---|---|---|---|---|---|---|---|---|---|
| 1 | 1 | 2 | 3 | 4 | 5 | 6 | 7 | 8 | 9 | 10 |
| 2 | 2 | 4 | 6 | 8 | 10 | 12 | 14 | 16 | 18 | 20 |
| 3 | 3 | 6 | 9 | 12 | 15 | 18 | 21 | 24 | 27 | 30 |
| 4 | 4 | 8 | 12 | 16 | 20 | 24 | 28 | 32 | 36 | 40 |
| 5 | 5 | 10 | 15 | 20 | 25 | 30 | 35 | 40 | 45 | 50 |
| 6 | 6 | 12 | 18 | 24 | 30 | 36 | 42 | 48 | 54 | 60 |
| 7 | 7 | 14 | 21 | 28 | 35 | 42 | 49 | 56 | 63 | 70 |
| 8 | 8 | 16 | 24 | 32 | 40 | 48 | 56 | 64 | 72 | 80 |
| 9 | 9 | 18 | 27 | 36 | 45 | 54 | 63 | 72 | 81 | 90 |
| 10 | 10 | 20 | 30 | 40 | 50 | 60 | 70 | 80 | 90 | 100 |

Use with Lesson 3.1.

## Math Boxes 3.1

**1.** Put these numbers in order from smallest to largest.

     0.6       0.06       0.43       0.9

_____

_____

_____

_____

**2.** Name as many line segments as you can in the figure below.

$A$     $B$        $C$  $D$

_____

_____

_____

**3.** Add.

**a.** $459 + 291 =$ _____

**b.** _____ $= 389 + 712$

**c.** _____ $= 120 + 880$

**d.** $72 + 63 =$ _____

# Patterns in Multiplication Facts

**Math Message**

Look at the table on journal page 52.

1. Find a pattern in the 9s multiplication facts. Describe the pattern.

   _____

   _____

   _____

   _____

2. Find a pattern in the 5s multiplication facts. Describe the pattern.

   _____

   _____

   _____

   _____

3. What other patterns can you find in the multiplication facts? Write about some of them.

   _____

   _____

   _____

   _____

   _____

# Math Boxes 3.2

**1.** Which amount below is closest to the sum of $2.50, $0.75, $3.85, and $12.70? Circle the amount.

$5.00

$10.00

$15.00

$20.00

SRB
155

**2.** Number of days it took 10 students to complete their science projects:

6, 4, 10, 11, 8, 6, 14, 9, 3, 12

**a.** What is the range for this set of numbers? _____

**b.** What is the median? _____

SRB
65

**3.** Subtract.

**a.** _____ = 81 − 46

**b.** _____ = 372 − 84

**c.** 602 − 213 = _____

**d.** 420 − 167 = _____

SRB
11-14

## Math Boxes 3.3

**1.** Put these numbers in order from smallest to largest.

  0.7          0.007          0.5          0.63

  _____

  _____

  _____

  _____

**2.** Name as many line segments as you can in the figure below.

  E        F              G  H

  _____

  _____

  _____

**3.** Add.

  **a.** 379 + 685 = _____

  **b.** _____ = 208 + 397

  **c.** _____ = 230 + 570

  **d.** 34 + 76 = _____

Use with Lesson 3.3.

# Multiplication and Division

| Equivalents | | | |
|---|---|---|---|
| 3 * 4 | 12 / 3 | 12 ÷ 3 | 3 < 5 (< means "is less than") |
| 3 × 4 | $\frac{12}{3}$ | 3)12 | 5 > 3 (> means "is greater than") |

**1.** Choose 3 Fact Triangles. Write the fact family for each.

_____ * _____ = _____  |  _____ × _____ = _____  |  _____ * _____ = _____

_____ * _____ = _____  |  _____ × _____ = _____  |  _____ * _____ = _____

_____ / _____ = _____  |  _____ / _____ = _____  |  _____ ÷ _____ = _____

_____ / _____ = _____  |  _____ / _____ = _____  |  _____ ÷ _____ = _____

**2.** Solve each division fact.

**a.** 27 / 3 = _____        Think: How many 3s in 27?

**b.** _____ = 45 / 5        Think: How many 5s in 45?

**c.** 36 ÷ 6 = _____        Think: 6 times what number equals 36?

**d.** 24 / 8 = _____        Think: 8 times what number equals 24?

**3.** A cashier has 5 rolls of quarters and 6 rolls of dimes in his cash register. Each roll of quarters is worth $10, and each roll of dimes is worth $5.

**a.** How much are the rolls of quarters and dimes worth in all?        $_____

**b.** How many quarters are in 1 roll?        _____ quarters

**c.** How many quarters are in the 5 rolls?        _____ quarters

**d.** How many dimes are in 1 roll?        _____ dimes

**e.** How many dimes are in the 6 rolls?        _____ dimes

**f.** There is also $7.50 worth of half-dollars in the cash register. How many half-dollars is that?        _____ half-dollars

# Math Boxes 3.4

**1.** Which amount below is closest to the sum of $1.80, $3.75, $1.85, and $1.70? Circle the amount.

$5.00

$10.00

$15.00

$20.00

**2.** Number of glasses of milk drunk by 10 students in a week:

16, 13, 15, 20, 8, 10, 15, 12, 10, 18

**a.** What is the range for this set of numbers? _____

**b.** What is the median? _____

**3.** Subtract.

**a.** _____ = 72 − 35

**b.** _____ = 489 − 95

**c.** 503 − 121 = _____

**d.** 830 − 342 = _____

Use with Lesson 3.4.

# Math Boxes 3.5

---

**1.** Riley estimated the height of his classroom ceiling. Circle the most reasonable estimate.

7 meters

3 meters

20 meters

SRB 110

---

**2.** Complete the "What's My Rule?" table and state the rule.

Rule _____

| in | out |
|----|-----|
| 9  | 63  |
| 3  | 21  |
| 10 |     |
|    | 56  |
| 2  |     |

SRB 142-146

---

**3.** Solve.

a.  729
  + 432

b.  9,004
  − 515

SRB 9-14

---

**4.** A number has

2 in the tens place,
8 in the hundred-thousands place,
5 in the millions place,
7 in the hundreds place,
9 in the ones place,
4 in the thousands place, and
1 in the ten-thousands place.

Write the number:

____ , ____ ____ ____ , ____ ____ ____

SRB 4

---

**5. a.** Measure the line segment to the nearest $\frac{1}{4}$ inch.

_____

P                                                    Q

_____ inches

**b.** Draw a line segment $4\frac{1}{4}$ inches long.

SRB 108

---

# Measuring Air Distances

Estimate which city listed below is the closest
to Washington, D.C.                                    _____

Estimate which city is the farthest.                   _____

**Air distance from Washington, D.C. to:**

Cairo, Egypt                              About _____ miles

Mexico City, Mexico                       About _____ miles

Stockholm, Sweden                         About _____ miles

Moscow, Russia                            About _____ miles

Tokyo, Japan                              About _____ miles

Shanghai, China                           About _____ miles

Sydney, Australia                         About _____ miles

Warsaw, Poland                            About _____ miles

Cape Town, South Africa                   About _____ miles

Rio de Janeiro, Brazil                    About _____ miles

Choose your own city. _____   About _____ miles

---

### Earth

The distance around the equator is about 42 million times the distance
around a globe with a 12-inch diameter.

If Earth were a huge, empty ball, it would be possible to fill it with about
50,000,000,000,000,000,000,000 twelve-inch globes. This number is read
as "50 sextillion." Another way to write this number is $5 * 10^{22}$. This is read
as "5 times 10 to the 22nd power."

# Math Boxes 3.6

---

**1.** What numbers come next?

   **a.** 0.1, 0.2, 0.3, _____, _____, _____

   **b.** 1.4, 1.6, 1.8, _____, _____, _____

   **c.** 3, 2.5, 2, _____, _____, _____

   **d.** 6.72, 6.73, 6.74, _____, _____,

      _____

**2.** Add or subtract.

   **a.** $3.56 + $2.49 = _____

   **b.** $0.67 + $0.08 = _____

   **c.** $6.25 − $5.01 = _____

   **d.** $3.37 − $0.24 = _____

34 35

---

**3.** Complete the "What's My Rule?" table and state the rule.

   *Rule* _____

| in | out |
|----|-----|
| 40 | 5 |
| 24 | 3 |
| 64 |   |
|    | 4 |
|    | 9 |

145

**4.** If 1 centimeter on a map represents 20 kilometers, then

   **a.** 2 cm represent _____ km.

   **b.** 8 cm represent _____ km.

   **c.** 5 mm represent _____ km.

   **d.** 3.5 cm represent _____ km.

   **e.** 6.5 cm represent _____ km.

125

---

**5.** A rock collector has 136 rocks in her collection. She took them to a geologist who said that 57 of them are not valuable. How many of them are valuable?

_____

132 152

**6.** Solve the riddle.

I am a four-sided polygon.

My two short sides are the same length and meet at a vertex.

My two long sides are the same length and meet at a vertex.

What am I? _____

86

---

# Flying to Cairo

Pretend that you are flying from Washington, D.C., to Cairo, Egypt. You have a choice of flying by way of Amsterdam, Holland, or by way of Rome, Italy. The air distances are shown in the table.

| Air Distance between Cities (in miles) | | |
|---|---|---|
| | Amsterdam | Rome |
| Washington, D.C. | 3,851 | 4,497 |
| Cairo | 2,035 | 1,326 |

If you fly first class, your ticket will cost $850. If you fly economy class, you will save $175.

1. About how many more miles is it from Washington, D.C., to Rome than from Washington, D.C., to Amsterdam?

   _____
   (number model)

   **Answer:** About _____ miles

2. What is the total distance from Washington, D.C., to Cairo by way of Amsterdam?

   _____
   (number model)

   **Answer:** About _____ miles

3. What is the total distance from Washington, D.C., to Cairo by way of Rome?

   _____
   (number model)

   **Answer:** About _____ miles

                                           Use with Lesson 3.7.

# Flying to Cairo (cont.)

4. About how many fewer miles will you fly
   if you go by way of Rome rather than
   Amsterdam?

   _____
   (number model)

   **Answer:** About _____ miles

5. How much will your ticket cost if you fly
   economy class?

   _____
   (number model)

   **Answer:** _____

6. What is the total distance (round-trip) from
   Washington, D.C., to Cairo by way of
   Rome, and then from Cairo back to
   Washington, D.C., by way of Rome again?

   _____
   (number model)

   **Answer:** About _____ miles

7. One of the flights to Amsterdam leaves
   Washington, D.C., at 1:15 P.M. It lands in
   Amsterdam 8 hours and 45 minutes later.

   a. At what time does it land,
      Washington, D.C., time?

   **Answer:** _____ (A.M. or P.M.?)

   b. At what time does it land, Amsterdam time?
      (Use the Time Zones map on pages 220
      and 221 in the World Tour section of
      your *Student Reference Book.*)

   **Answer:** _____ (A.M. or P.M.?)

# Math Boxes 3.7

1. Sara measured the length of her arm. Circle the most reasonable measurement.

   5 centimeters

   50 centimeters

   150 centimeters

2. Complete the "What's My Rule?" table and state the rule.

   Rule _____

   | in | out |
   |----|-----|
   | 2  | 8   |
   | 6  | 24  |
   |    | 32  |
   | 4  |     |
   |    | 20  |

3. Solve.

   a.  604
      + 817

   b.  3,005
      − 686

4. A number has

   1 in the tens place,
   3 in the hundreds place,
   5 in the ones place,
   7 in the hundred-thousands place,
   9 in the thousands place,
   2 in the ten-thousands place, and
   4 in the millions place.

   Write the number:

   ____, ____ ____ ____, ____ ____ ____

5. a. Measure the line segment to the nearest $\frac{1}{4}$ inch.

   B _____ L

   _____ inches

   b. Draw a line segment $4\frac{3}{4}$ inches long.

Use with Lesson 3.7.

Date _____                    Time _____

# Number Sentences

Tell whether each sentence below is true or false. If it is not possible to tell, write "can't tell" on the answer blank.

**1.** $28 - 16 = 12$ _____    **2.** $7 + 3 < 1$ _____

**3.** $6 = 36 \div 6$ _____    **4.** $27 + 3 = 5 * 6$ _____

**5.** $80 - ? = 40$ _____    **6.** $0 = 4 / 4$ _____

**7.** $3 * 8 < 30$ _____    **8.** $2 \times 7$ _____

**9.** Make up 5 true number sentences and 5 false number sentences. Mix them up. Ask your partner to tell whether each sentence is true or false.

| Equivalents | | | |
|---|---|---|---|
| $3 * 4$ | $12 / 3$ | $12 \div 3$ | $3 < 5$ (< means "is less than") |
| $3 \times 4$ | $\frac{12}{3}$ | $3\overline{)12}$ | $5 > 3$ (> means "is greater than") |

**a.** _____

**b.** _____

**c.** _____

**d.** _____

**e.** _____

**f.** _____

**g.** _____

**h.** _____

**i.** _____

**j.** _____

# Elapsed Time

During a solar eclipse, the moon passes between the sun and Earth and casts a shadow across the surface of Earth. When this happens, it gets darker, as if it were dusk, even if the eclipse occurs in the middle of the day.

Total solar eclipses, in which the moon blocks out the entire sun, are very rare. A near-total eclipse, in which about 90% of the sun is hidden from view, occurred over part of the United States on May 10, 1994. Before that, the most recent total eclipse visible in the continental United States occurred in 1979.

**1.** How many years had passed between these two eclipses? _____ years

The next total solar eclipse will not be seen over the United States until 2017.

**2.** How old will you be then? _____ years old

**3.** How much time passed from the start to the middle of the eclipse?

_____

**Hint:**

From 10:24 to 11:00 → _____ hour _____ minutes

From 11:00 to 12:04 → _____ hour _____ minutes

Total → _____ hour _____ minutes

**4.** How much time passed from the middle to the end of the eclipse? _____

**5.** How long did the eclipse last? _____

### Eclipses

People in ancient times were afraid of solar eclipses. The Chinese thought the eclipse was caused by a dragon swallowing the sun. They would bang on pans and shoot arrows into the sky to scare the dragon. The Japanese believed that poison fell from the sky. They would cover their wells to prevent the poison from getting into their drinking water.

# Math Boxes 3.8

---

**1.** What numbers come next?

   **a.** 0.5, 0.8, 1.1, _____, _____, _____

   **b.** 2.7, 3.2, 3.7, _____, _____, _____

   **c.** 4, 3.8, 3.6, _____, _____, _____

   **d.** 5.05, 5.06, 5.07, _____, _____,

     _____

---

**2.** Add or subtract.

   **a.** $10.97 + $15.60 = _____

   **b.** $1.23 + $7.00 = _____

   **c.** $4.56 − $2.07 = _____

   **d.** $1.85 − $1.53 = _____

---

**3.** Complete the "What's My Rule?" table and state the rule.

Rule _____

| in | out |
|----|-----|
| 45 | 5 |
| 81 | 9 |
|    | 3 |
|    | 4 |
| 72 |   |

---

**4.** If 1 inch on a map represents 30 miles, then

   **a.** 3 inches represent _____ miles.

   **b.** 9 inches represent _____ miles.

   **c.** $\frac{1}{2}$ inch represents _____ miles.

   **d.** $5\frac{1}{2}$ inches represent _____ miles.

   **e.** 1 foot represents _____ miles.

---

**5.** The statue of Chief Crazy Horse in South Dakota is 563 feet tall. The Statue of Liberty is 151 feet tall. What is the difference in height of the two statues?

   _____ feet

---

**6.** Solve the riddle.

I am a polygon.

All my angles have the same measure.

Each of my 5 sides has the same measure.

What am I? _____

---

# Parentheses in Number Sentences

## Part 1

Make a true sentence by filling in the missing number.

1. a. $(30 - 15) * 2 =$ _____     b. $30 - (15 * 2) =$ _____

2. a. _____ $= 28 / (14 / 2)$     b. _____ $= (28 / 14) / 2$

3. a. $(6 + 8) / (2 - 1) =$ _____     b. $6 + (8 / 2) - 1 =$ _____

## Part 2

Make a true sentence by inserting parentheses.

4. a. $4 \times 9 - 2 = 34$     b. $4 \times 9 - 2 = 28$

5. a. $24 = 53 - 11 + 18$     b. $60 = 53 - 11 + 18$

6. a. $12 / 4 + 2 = 2$     b. $12 / 4 + 2 = 5$

7. a. $55 = 15 + 10 \times 4$     b. $100 = 15 + 10 \times 4$

## Challenge

8. a. $10 - 4 / 2 * 3 = 24$     b. $10 - 4 / 2 * 3 = 1$

## Part 3

Pretend you are playing a game of *Name That Number* with only 3 cards per hand.
To name the target number, use all 3 numbers and any operations you want.
For each problem, write a true number sentence, containing parentheses, using the
3 numbers and the target number.

9. Use: 2, 5, 15   Target number: 5   _____

10. Use: 3, 4, 5   Target number: 17   _____

11. Use: 1, 3, 11   Target number: 4   _____

Use with Lesson 3.9.

## Math Boxes 3.9

1. a. Measure the line segment to the nearest centimeter.

   _____

   B                                                    N

   _____ cm

   b. Draw a line segment that is half the length of $\overline{BN}$.

   c. How long is the line segment you drew? _____ cm

SRB
108

2. QUARTZY is the highest scoring word in a popular board game; it is worth 164 points. BEZIQUE is the second-highest scoring word, worth 161 points. If you were able to use both words, what would your score be?

   _____ points

SRB
132  152

3. Complete the multiplication facts.

   a.  $4 * 5 =$ _____

   b.  $6 * 6 =$ _____

   c.  _____ $= 8 * 3$

   d.  _____ $= 6 * 7$

   e.  _____ $= 5 * 5$

   f.  $6 * 8 =$ _____

4. Tell whether each number sentence is true or false.

   a.  $55 = 10 + (5 * 7)$ _____

   b.  $74 = (4 * 7) + (7 * 6)$ _____

   c.  $68 > (9 * 4) + 13$ _____

   d.  $4 = (8 * 7) / (12 + 2)$ _____

SRB
130

5. Make a true sentence by inserting parentheses.

   a.  $8 * 2 + 20 = 36$

   b.  $63 = 9 / 3 * 21$

   c.  $28 / 7 * 4 = 16$

   d.  $10 / 5 * 2 = 1$

SRB
129

# Broken Calculator

Solve each open sentence on your calculator without using the "broken" key.
Record your steps.

**1.**

| Broken Key: $\ominus$ | |
|---|---|
| To Solve: $68 + x = 413$ | |
| | |
| | |
| | |
| | |

**2.**

| Broken Key: $\div$ | |
|---|---|
| To Solve: $s * 48 = 2{,}928$ | |
| | |
| | |
| | |
| | |

**3.**

| Broken Key: $\ominus$ | |
|---|---|
| To Solve: $z + 643 = 1{,}210$ | |
| | |
| | |
| | |
| | |

**4.**

| Broken Key: $\otimes$ | |
|---|---|
| To Solve: $w\ /\ 15 = 8$ | |
| | |
| | |
| | |
| | |

**6.** Make up one for your partner to solve.

**5.**

| Broken Key: $\oplus$ | |
|---|---|
| To Solve: $d - 574 = 1{,}437$ | |
| | |
| | |
| | |
| | |

| Broken Key: | |
|---|---|
| To Solve: | |
| | |
| | |
| | |
| | |

Use with Lesson 3.10.

# Open Sentences

Solve each open sentence. Copy the sentence over, with the solution in place of the variable. Circle the solution.

**1.** $51 = n + 29$

$$51 = \boxed{22} + 29$$

**2.** $48 + d = 70$

_____

**3.** $34 - x = 7$

_____

**4.** $32 = 76 - p$

_____

**5.** $b - 7 = 12$

_____

**6.** $u - 30 = 10$

_____

**7.** $y = 3 * 8$

_____

**8.** $5 * m = 35$

_____

**9.** $21 / x = 7$

_____

**10.** $x = 32 / 8$

_____

**11.** $5 = w / 10$

_____

**12.** $h - 6 = 9$

_____

# Math Boxes 3.10

**1.** What numbers come next?

   **a.** 0.2, 0.6, 1, _____, _____, _____

   **b.** 5.6, 5.9, 6.2, _____, _____, _____

   **c.** 8, 7.4, 6.8, _____, _____, _____

   **d.** 7.03, 7.08, 7.13, _____, _____,

      _____

**2.** Add or subtract.

   **a.** $14.99 + $2.80 = _____

   **b.** $1.46 + $8.12 = _____

   **c.** $5.87 − $2.15 = _____

   **d.** $1.74 − $1.23 = _____

**3.** Complete the "What's My Rule?" table and state the rule.

   *Rule* _____

| in | out |
|----|-----|
| 24 | 8   |
| 9  | 3   |
|    | 6   |
|    | 7   |
| 15 |     |

**4.** If $\frac{1}{2}$ inch on a map represents 5 miles, then

   **a.** 1 in. represents _____ mi.

   **b.** $4\frac{1}{2}$ in. represent _____ mi.

   **c.** _____ in. represent 15 mi.

   **d.** _____ in. represent 30 mi.

   **e.** _____ in. represents $2\frac{1}{2}$ mi.

**5.** The area of Rhode Island is 1,545 square miles. The area of Delaware is 2,489 square miles. How much greater is the area of Delaware than of Rhode Island?

   _____ square miles

**6.** Solve the riddle.

   I am a polygon.

   I have two right angles.

   I have only one pair of parallel sides.

   What am I? _____

# Logic Problems

**Math Message**

1. There are three children in the Smith family: Sara, Sam, and Sue.
   Use the following clues to find each one's age:

   • Each of the two younger children is half as old as the next older child.

   • The oldest is 16.

   • Sara is not the oldest.

   • Sara is twice as old as Sam.

   What is the age of each person?

   Sara _____   Sam _____   Sue _____

---

2. a. DeeAnn, Eric, Brooke, and Kelsey all have a favorite sport. Each one likes a
      different sport. Their favorite sports are basketball, swimming, golf, and tennis.

      • DeeAnn doesn't like water.

      • Both Eric and Brooke like to hit a ball.

      • Eric doesn't like to play on a playing field that has lines on it.

      What is each person's favorite sport?

      DeeAnn _____        Eric _____

      Brooke _____        Kelsey _____

   b. Write an explanation of how your group found the answers.

      _____

      _____

      _____

      _____

      _____

      _____

# Logic Problems (cont.)

3.  Raoul, Martha, Kwan, and Karen like to draw. One of them likes working with colored markers best, another with watercolor paints, another with colored chalk, and another with colored pencils.

    • Raoul does not like to work with paintbrushes.

    • Martha likes to sharpen her drawing tools.

    • Kwan and Karen do not like dust.

    • Karen sometimes gets bristles in her artwork.

    Find out what each child likes best. Use the logic grid to help you.

|  | Colored markers | Watercolor paints | Colored chalk | Colored pencils |
|---|---|---|---|---|
| **Raoul** |  |  |  |  |
| **Martha** |  |  |  |  |
| **Kwan** |  |  |  |  |
| **Karen** |  |  |  |  |

Raoul _____     Martha _____

Kwan _____     Karen _____

Use with Lesson 3.11.

# Logic Problems (cont.)

4. Sam, Don, Darla, Jon, and Sara all have a favorite kind of cookie.
   They each like a different kind best.

   • Sam and Jon do not like peanut butter.

   • Don has never tried sugar cookies and neither has Sara.

   • Darla does not like raisins.

   • Jon doesn't like sugar cookies.

   • Darla and Jon do not like chocolate.

   • Sara does like chocolate.

   • Don likes cinnamon.

   What kind of cookie does each like best? Use the logic grid to help you.

   | | Peanut butter | Sugar | Cinnamon | Oatmeal raisin | Chocolate |
   |---|---|---|---|---|---|
   | **Sam** | | | | | |
   | **Don** | | | | | |
   | **Darla** | | | | | |
   | **Jon** | | | | | |
   | **Sara** | | | | | |

   Sam _____      Don _____

   Darla _____      Jon _____

   Sara _____

# Estimating Distances

You want to take a trip to Egypt and see the following sights:

• Cairo, the capital, on the Nile River, near the Pyramids at Giza

• Alexandria, a busy modern city and port on the Mediterranean

• the Aswan High Dam across the Nile River, completed in 1970, and Lake Nasser, which formed behind the dam

• the temples at Abu Simbel, built more than 3,000 years ago, which were moved to their present location in the 1960s to escape the rising water of Lake Nasser

You want to know how far it is between locations.

1. The distance between Alexandria and Abu Simbel is about _____ inches on the map.

   That is about _____ miles.

2. The distance between Cairo and Aswan is about _____ inches on the map.

   That is about _____ miles.

3. The distance between Abu Simbel and Aswan is about _____ inch(es) on the map.

   That is about _____ miles.

Use with Lesson 3.11.

# Math Boxes 3.11

---

**1.** **a.** Measure the line segment to the nearest centimeter.

_____

L                                                                                    P

_____ cm

**b.** Draw a line segment that is half the length of $\overline{LP}$.

**c.** How long is the line segment you drew? _____ cm

---

**2.** There were 123 recipients of the Congressional Medal of Honor for World War I and 433 for World War II. How many of these medals in all were issued for the two wars?

_____ medals

**3.** Complete the multiplication facts.

**a.** $4 * 7 =$ _____

**b.** $7 * 7 =$ _____

**c.** $5 * 7 =$ _____

**d.** _____ $= 3 * 6$

**e.** _____ $= 6 * 5$

**f.** _____ $= 9 * 6$

---

**4.** Tell whether each number sentence is true or false.

**a.** $(7 * 4) - 2 = 80 - (9 * 6)$ _____

**b.** $8 * 11 = (8 * 5) + (8 * 6)$ _____

**c.** $34 < (3 * 5) + (63 / 9)$ _____

**d.** $12 = (6 * 7) / (19 - 7)$ _____

**5.** Make a true sentence by inserting parentheses.

**a.** $7 * 4 - 4 = 0$

**b.** $45 / 9 + 10 = 15$

**c.** $8 * 7 - 6 = 8$

**d.** $24 / 3 + 5 = 13$

---

Use with Lesson 3.11.

# Time to Reflect

1. Why are multiplication turn-around facts called "turn-around facts"?

   _____

   _____

   _____

   _____

   _____

2. In this unit, your teacher encouraged you to use "A Guide for Solving Number Stories" when solving problems. Do you think the steps and suggestions in the guide are useful? Why or why not?

   _____

   _____

   _____

   _____

   _____

3. Is the World Tour Project a good way to learn about numbers? Is it helping you? Why or why not?

   _____

   _____

   _____

   _____

   _____

Use with Lesson 3.12.

# Math Boxes 3.12

**1.** Put these numbers in order from smallest to largest.

    0.8        0.08        0.73        0.095

_____

_____

_____

_____

**2.** What numbers come next?

**a.** 0.1, 0.9, 1.7, _____, _____, _____

**b.** 5.6, 5.3, 5, _____, _____, _____

**c.** 8, 6.9, 5.8, _____, _____, _____

**d.** 7.23, 7.28, 7.33, _____, _____,

_____

**3.** Add or subtract.

**a.** $11.03 + $4.79 = _____

**b.** $3.62 + $7.25 = _____

**c.** $8.96 − $5.92 = _____

**d.** $3.56 − $2.89 = _____

**4.** Blake estimated the length of his little finger. Circle the most reasonable estimate.

20 millimeters

45 millimeters

80 millimeters

**5. a.** Measure the line segment to the nearest centimeter.

_____

*A*                                        *B*

_____ cm

**b.** Draw a line segment that is half the length of $\overline{AB}$.

**c.** How long is the line segment you drew? _____ cm

# Tenths and Hundredths

| Base-10 Block | Symbol | Value |
|---|---|---|
| Flat | □ | 1 |
| Long | \| | $\frac{1}{10}$, or 0.1 |
| Cube | . | $\frac{1}{100}$, or 0.01 |

**1.** Complete the table.

| Base-10 Blocks | Fraction Notation | Decimal Notation |
|---|---|---|
| \|\| | $\frac{2}{10}$ | 0.2 |
| ::::.. | | |
| \|\|\|\|\| \|\|\|\| | | |
| □ \|\|\| :.... | | |

**2.** Write each number in decimal notation.

*Example* $\frac{3}{10}$ = __0.3__

**a.** $\frac{4}{10}$ = _____     **b.** $\frac{71}{100}$ = _____     **c.** $32\frac{6}{100}$ = _____

**3.** Draw base-10 blocks to show each number. Draw as few blocks as possible.

*Example* 0.3 \|\|\|

**a.** 0.43       **b.** 2.16

**4.** Write each of the following in decimal notation.

**a.** 9 tenths _____    **b.** 82 hundredths _____    **c.** 38 and 5 tenths _____

         Use with Lesson 4.1.

# Problem-Solving Practice

1. Fifteen fourth graders were asked how many blocks they lived from school. The results are displayed in the following graph:

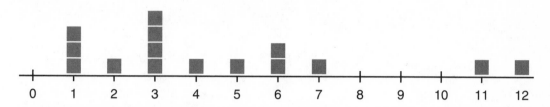

a. What is the maximum number of blocks any student lives from school? _____

b. What is the minimum number of blocks? _____

c. What is the range? _____

d. What is the mode? _____

e. What is the median? _____

For Problems 2–4, use the computation grid if you wish.

2. The Goldmans are taking a 350-mile trip. If they drive 185 miles before lunch, how much farther will they have to go?

Number model:

_____

Answer: _____ miles

3. A doughnut costs 45 cents. Milk costs 35 cents a carton. How much will 2 doughnuts and 1 carton of milk cost?

Number model:

_____

Answer: $_____

4. 407 − 192 = _____

# Math Boxes 4.1

---

**1.** Which of the following is closest to the sum of 458, 1,999, and 12,307?

5,000

10,000

15,000

20,000

155 156

**2.** Complete the multiplication and division facts.

a. 6 * _____ = 18

b. 3 * _____ = 21

c. 16 ÷ 4 = _____

d. 20 ÷ 5 = _____

e. 54 ÷ 6 = _____

258

f. 9 * 4 = _____

---

**3.** Solve.

a. $323 - y = 42$     $y =$ _____

b. $199 = p - 408$     $p =$ _____

c. $r + 115 = 655$     $r =$ _____

d. $430 + s = 700$     $s =$ _____

128

**4.** In the numeral 59.378, the 5 stands for 5 tens.

a. The 9 stands for _____.

b. The 3 stands for _____.

c. The 7 stands for _____.

d. The 8 stands for _____.

28  29

---

**5.** Draw and label ray *BY*.

Draw point *A* on it.

77

**6.** Make true sentences by inserting parentheses.

a.     5  *  4  -  2  =  18

b.     25  +  8  *  7  =  81

c.     1  =  36  /  6  -  5

d.     24  =  81  /  9  +  15

129

---

Use with Lesson 4.1.

# Comparing Decimals

**Math Message**

1. Arjun thought that 0.3 was less than 0.15. How could you help Arjun see that 0.3 is more than 0.15?

   _____

   _____

   _____

   _____

2. Use base-10 blocks to complete the following table.

   "<" means "is less than."

   ">" means "is greater than."

| Base-10 Blocks | Decimal | >, <, or = | Decimal | Base-10 Blocks |
|:---:|:---:|:---:|:---:|:---:|
| &#124;&#124; | 0.2 | > | 0.12 | &#124; .. |
| ..... | | | 0.1 | |
| | 0.13 | | | &#124;&#124;&#124; . |
| &#124;&#124;&#124; .... | | | 0.3 | |
| | 1.2 | | | □ □ &#124; |
| &#124;&#124;&#124;&#124;::... | | | 0.39 | |
| | 2.3 | | | □ &#124;&#124;&#124;&#124;&#124;&#124; &#124;&#124;&#124;&#124;&#124;&#124; &#124;&#124;&#124; |

# Ordering Decimals

1. Write < or >.

    a. 0.24 _____ 0.18     b. 0.05 _____ 0.1     c. 0.2 _____ 0.35

    d. 1.03 _____ 0.30     e. 3.2 _____ 6.59     f. 25.9 _____ 25.72

2. Put these numbers in order from smallest to largest.

    a. 0.05, 0.5, 0.55, 5.5     _____ _____ _____ _____
                                           smallest                             largest

    b. 0.99, 0.27, 1.8, 2.01     _____ _____ _____ _____
                                           smallest                             largest

    c. 2.1, 2.01, 20.1, 20.01     _____ _____ _____ _____
                                           smallest                             largest

    d. 0.01, 0.10, 0.11, 0.09     _____ _____ _____ _____
                                           smallest                             largest

3. "What's green inside, white outside, and hops?"
    To find the answer, put the numbers in order from smallest to largest.

| 0.66 | 1 | 0.2 | 1.05 | 0.90 | 0.01 | 0.75 | 0.35 | $\frac{1}{4}$ | $\frac{1}{2}$ | 0.05 | 0.09 | 5.5 |
|------|---|-----|------|------|------|------|------|---------------|---------------|------|------|-----|
| N | I | O | C | W | A | D | S | G | A | F | R | H |

Write your answers in the following table. The first answer is done for you.

| 0.01 | | | | | | | | | | | | |
|------|---|---|---|---|---|---|---|---|---|---|---|---|
| A | | | | | | | | | | | | |

# Math Boxes 4.2

---

**1. Complete.**

a. $5 * 3 =$ _____

b. $5 * 30 =$ _____

c. _____ $= 5 * 9$

d. _____ $= 50 * 9$

e. $8 * 9 =$ _____

f. $8 * 90 =$ _____

SRB
16

---

**2. If $\frac{1}{4}$ inch on a map represents 40 miles, then**

a. $\frac{1}{2}$ in. represents _____ mi.

b. 1 in. represents _____ mi.

c. $1\frac{3}{4}$ in. represent _____ mi.

d. 2 in. represent _____ mi.

e. $2\frac{1}{4}$ in. represent _____ mi.

SRB
125

---

**3. Insert >, <, or =.**

a. 0.96 _____ 0.4

b. 0.50 _____ 0.500

c. 1.3 _____ 1.09

d. 0.85 _____ 0.86

SRB
30 31

---

**4. Add or subtract.**

a.
$$
\begin{array}{r}
391 \\
+\ 467 \\
\hline
\end{array}
$$

b.
$$
\begin{array}{r}
983 \\
-\ 494 \\
\hline
\end{array}
$$

SRB
9-14

---

**5. Ray, Samantha, Josh, and Erica each have a different favorite after-school snack: ice cream, pretzels, potato chips, or cookies. Find out which snack is the favorite for each child.** (*Hint:* Use a logic grid if you need help.)

• Josh does not like salty snacks.

• Ray likes a snack that is cold and comes in many different flavors.

• Samantha likes a snack that is salty and may sometimes be twisted.

Ray _____          Samantha _____

Josh _____          Erica _____

---

# Uses of Decimals

## Math Message

Describe two examples in which decimals are used in real life.

_____

_____

_____

## A Bicycle Trip

Bill and Alex often took all-day bicycle trips together.

During the summer, they took a 3-day bicycle tour. They carried camping gear in their saddlebags for the two nights they would be away from home.

Alex had a **trip meter** that showed miles traveled, in tenths of miles. He kept a log of the distances they traveled each day, before and after lunch.

| Travel Log | | |
|---|---|---|
| | Distance Traveled | |
| Timetable | Before lunch | After lunch |
| Day 1 | 27.0 mi | 31.3 mi |
| Day 2 | 36.6 mi | 20.9 mi |
| Day 3 | 25.8 mi | 27.0 mi |

Use estimation to answer the following questions. Do not work the problems on paper or with a calculator.

1. On which day did they travel the most miles?              _____

2. On which day did they travel the fewest miles?           _____

3. During the whole trip, did they travel more miles
   before or after lunch?                                             _____

4. Estimate the total distance they traveled. Circle your estimate.

   a. less than 150 miles            b. between 150 and 180 miles

   c. between 180 and 200 miles      d. more than 200 miles

5. On Day 1, about how many more miles did
   they travel after lunch than before lunch?  _____

6. Bill said that they traveled 1.2 more miles before
   lunch on Day 1 than on Day 3. Alex disagreed.
   He said they traveled 2.2 more miles. Who is right?  _____

Use with Lesson 4.3.

## Math Boxes 4.3

---

**1.** Which of the following is closest to the sum of 3,005, 865, and 2,109?

5,000

10,000

15,000

20,000

---

**2.** Complete the multiplication and division facts.

**a.** 9 * _____ = 27

**b.** 5 * _____ = 40

**c.** 42 ÷ 6 = _____

**d.** 54 ÷ 9 = _____

**e.** 63 ÷ 7 = _____

**f.** 9 * 9 = _____

---

**3.** Solve.

**a.** 503 + $y$ = 642    $y$ = _____

**b.** $p$ + 263 = 319    $p$ = _____

**c.** $r$ − 320 = 600    $r$ = _____

**d.** 444 − $s$ = 93    $s$ = _____

---

**4.** In 34.561,

**a.** the 3 stands for _____.

**b.** the 4 stands for _____.

**c.** the 5 stands for _____.

**d.** the 6 stands for _____.

**e.** the 1 stands for _____.

---

**5.** Draw and label ray *CT*.

Draw point *A* on it.

---

**6.** Make true sentences by inserting parentheses.

**a.**   7 * 8 − 6 = 50

**b.**   13 − 4 * 6 = 54

**c.**   10 = 49 / 7 + 3

**d.**   28 = 42 / 7 + 22

---

Use with Lesson 4.3.

# Decimal Addition and Subtraction

## Math Message

What's wrong with this problem?  _____

What is the correct answer?  _____

$$
\begin{array}{r}
0.76 \\
+\ \ 0.2 \\
\hline
0.78
\end{array}
$$

_____

_____

_____

## Decimal Addition and Subtraction

Add or subtract. Show your work below.

**1.** $2.05 + 1.83 =$ _____

**2.** $3.04 - 2.8 =$ _____

**3.** $1 - 0.67 =$ _____

**4.** $2.4 + 3.01 + 0.26 =$ _____

**5.** $2.31 - 1.88 =$ _____

**6.** $19 + 1.9 =$ _____

Use with Lesson 4.4.

# Decimals on Grids

This grid is the whole.

Fractions and decimals can be shown by shading the grid.

*Example*

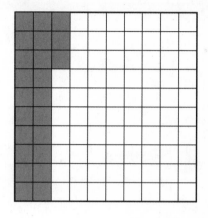

0.23, or $\frac{23}{100}$

Write a decimal and a fraction for each grid.

**1.**

0. _____  , or

**2.**

0. _____

Shade each grid to show the decimal.

**3.** 0.32

**4.** 0.05

# Math Boxes 4.4

---

**1.** Complete.

a. $6 * 9 = $ _____

b. $6 * 90 = $ _____

c. _____ $= 5 * 8$

d. _____ $= 50 * 8$

e. $4 * 4 = $ _____

f. $4 * 40 = $ _____

**2.** If 2 centimeters on a map represent 50 kilometers, then

a. 1 cm represents _____ km.

b. 3 cm represent _____ km.

c. 4 cm represent _____ km.

d. 7 cm represent _____ km.

e. 8 cm represent _____ km.

---

**3.** Insert $>$, $<$, or $=$.

a. 0.6 _____ 0.57

b. 0.37 _____ 0.36

c. 2.56 _____ 2.056

d. 0.24 _____ 0.240

**4.** Add or subtract.

a. $\begin{array}{r} 814 \\ + 123 \\ \hline \end{array}$

b. $\begin{array}{r} 754 \\ - 396 \\ \hline \end{array}$

---

**5.** Bill, Marta, Monique, and Louis each participate in a different after-school activity: hockey, dance, gymnastics, or swimming. Find out in which activity each child participates.

• Louis wears a lot of equipment for protection during his after-school activity.

• Marta wears tights and leotards for her after-school activity.

• Bill does not like to dance or be in the water.

Bill _____     Marta _____

Monique _____     Louis _____

---

# Using Decimals

## Math Message

Solve. Show your work below.

1. $18.09 + $7.24 = $_____

2. $3.78 + $5.22 = $_____

3. $24.61 − $19.38 = $_____

4. $12 − $1.47 = $_____

## Keeping a Bank Balance

On January 2, Kate's aunt opened a bank account for Kate. Her aunt deposited $100.00 in the account.

Over the next several months, Kate made regular deposits into her account. She deposited part of her allowance and most of the money she made babysitting.

Kate also made a few withdrawals—to buy a radio and some clothes.

Think about the answers to the following questions:

- When you **withdraw** money, do you take money out or put money in?

- When you **deposit** money, do you take money out or put money in?

- When your money earns **interest,** does this add money to your account or take money away?

# Keeping a Bank Balance (cont.)

The following table shows the transactions (deposits and withdrawals) that Kate made during the first 4 months of the year and the interest earned.

1. In March, Kate took more money out of her bank account than she put in. In which other month did she withdraw more money than she deposited? _____

2. Complete the table. Remember to **add** if Kate makes a deposit or earns interest and to **subtract** if she makes a withdrawal.

| Date | Transaction | | Current Balance |
|---|---|---|---|
| January 2 | Deposit | $100.00 | $ _100.00_ |
| January 14 | Deposit | $14.23 | + $ _14.23_ <br> $ _114.23_ |
| February 4 | Withdrawal | $16.50 | $ _____ <br> $ _____ |
| February 11 | Deposit | $33.75 | $ _____ <br> $ _____ |
| February 14 | Withdrawal | $16.50 | $ _____ <br> $ _____ |
| March 19 | Deposit | $62.00 | $ _____ <br> $ _____ |
| March 30 | Withdrawal | $104.26 | $ _____ <br> $ _____ |
| March 31 | Bank credited Kate's account with $0.78 in interest | | $ _____ <br> $ _____ |
| April 1 | Deposit | $70.60 | $ _____ <br> $ _____ |
| April 3 | Withdrawal | $45.52 | $ _____ <br> $ _____ |
| April 28 | Withdrawal | $27.91 | $ _____ <br> $ _____ |

Check your answers with a partner.

      Use with Lesson 4.5.

# Forming a Relay Team

Mrs. Wong, the gym teacher, wants to form 3 teams for a 200-yard relay race. There will be 4 students on each team. Each student will run 50 yards.

The table at the right shows how long it took some fourth-grade students to run 50 yards the last time they had a race. They were timed to the nearest tenth of a second.

Mrs. Wong will use these times to try to predict about how long it would take various combinations of students to run the 200-yard relay race.

Here are some combinations she tried. If she uses the times shown in the table, about how long (to the nearest tenth of a second) would the following teams take to run the 200-yard relay race?

| Runner | Time (seconds) |
|--------|----------------|
| Art | 6.3 |
| Bruce | 7.0 |
| Jamal | 7.4 |
| Doug | 7.9 |
| Al | 8.3 |
| Will | 8.8 |
| Linda | 6.2 |
| Sue | 7.6 |
| Pat | 7.7 |
| Mary | 8.1 |
| Alba | 8.4 |
| Joyce | 8.5 |

1. Art, Bruce, Jamal, Doug         About _____._____ seconds

2. the 4 fastest girls         About _____._____ seconds

3. the 4 slowest students         About _____._____ seconds

4. the 4 fastest students         About _____._____ seconds

5. the 2 fastest and the 2 slowest students         About _____._____ seconds

6. About how many yards per second did Bruce run?      _____ yards per second

## Challenge

7. Make up 3 teams that will be fairly evenly matched.

                                                     Estimated time

Team 1: _____      About _____._____ seconds

Team 2: _____      About _____._____ seconds

Team 3: _____      About _____._____ seconds

# Math Boxes 4.5

---

**1.** Add.

| | | | |
|---|---|---|---|
| **a.** | 6 | **b.** | 54 |
| | 40 | | 180 |
| | 150 | | 240 |
| | + 1,000 | | + 800 |

SRB
9 10

---

**2.** Complete the multiplication and division facts.

**a.** 7 * _____ = 28

**b.** 48 ÷ _____ = 8

**c.** _____ ÷ 8 = 7

**d.** _____ * 10 = 50

**e.** 8 * _____ = 64

---

**3.** Solve each open sentence.

**a.** 9.4 − K = 3    K = _____

**b.** 2.34 = S + 1.06    S = _____

**c.** R − 12.2 = 4.65    R = _____

**d.** 0.81 − M = 0.43    M = _____

**e.** F − 2.1 = 6.8    F = _____

SRB
128

---

**4.** Add 9 tens, 8 hundredths, and 3 tenths to 34.53.

What is the result? _____

SRB
34

---

**5.** Write as dollars and cents.

**a.** 20 dimes = $_____._____

**b.** 20 nickels = $_____._____

**c.** 20 quarters = $_____._____

**d.** 10 quarters and 7 dimes =

$_____._____

---

**6.** Make up a set of 5 numbers having the following landmarks:

median: 8

range: 10

minimum: 3

_____, _____, _____, _____, _____

SRB
65

---

Use with Lesson 4.5.

# Tenths, Hundredths, and Thousandths

**Math Message**

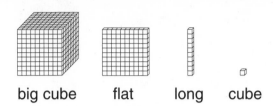

big cube    flat    long    cube

1 big cube = _____ flats

1 flat = $\dfrac{1}{\boxed{10}}$ of a big cube

1 big cube = _____ longs

1 long = $\dfrac{1}{\boxed{\phantom{00}}}$ of a big cube

1 big cube = _____ cubes

1 cube = $\dfrac{1}{\boxed{\phantom{00}}}$ of a big cube

| Base-10 Block | Symbol | Value |
|---|---|---|
| Big Cube | ▢ | 1 |
| Flat | □ | $\frac{1}{10}$, or 0.1 |
| Long | \| | $\frac{1}{100}$, or 0.01 |
| Cube | . | $\frac{1}{1,000}$, or 0.001 |

1. Complete the table.

| Base-10 Blocks | Fraction Notation | Decimal Notation |
|---|---|---|
| □ \|\|\|\| .. | $\frac{142}{1,000}$ | 0.142 |
| □□ ..... | | |
| \|\|\|\|\| \| | | |
| □□□□□ | | |
| ▢ \|\|\|\| ... | | |

# Tenths, Hundredths, and Thousandths (cont.)

2. Write each number in decimal notation.

Example $\frac{72}{1,000}$ = _0.072_

a. $\frac{416}{1,000}$ = _____     b. $\frac{17}{1,000}$ = _____     c. $\frac{8}{1,000}$ = _____

d. $7\frac{9}{100}$ = _____     e. $8\frac{14}{1,000}$ = _____     f. $385\frac{4}{10}$ = _____

3. Draw base-10 blocks to show each number.

Example 0.205

a. 0.21                              b. 0.306

c. 0.008                             d. 1.054

4. Write each of the following in decimal notation.

a. 284 thousandths _____     b. 36 hundredths _____

c. 7 thousandths _____     d. 90 and 16 thousandths _____

e. 15 and 3 tenths _____     f. 408 thousandths _____

5. Write < or >.

a. 0.302 _____ 0.203     b. 0.51 _____ 0.310     c. 0.816 _____ 0.9

d. 1.47 _____ 1.5     e. 0.073 _____ 0.73     f. 4.01 _____ 4.009

# Math Boxes 4.6

**1.** Write the following numbers using digits:

    **a.** three million, four hundred thirty-two

    thousand, nine _____

    **b.** six-hundred million, five thousand,

    twenty-one _____

SRB<br/>4

**2. a.** Measure the length of this line segment to the nearest centimeter.

    _____

    About _____ cm

    **b.** Draw a line segment 3 centimeters long.

SRB<br/>108

**3.** Put these numbers in order from smallest to largest.

    5.92      0.95      9.25      2.95      0.92

    _____ _____ _____ _____ _____

SRB<br/>30  31

**4.** A trumpeter swan can weigh about 16.8 kilograms. A Manchurian crane can weigh about 14.9 kilograms. How much heavier is a trumpeter swan than a Manchurian crane?

    _____ kilograms

SRB<br/>132  152

**5.** Add or subtract.

    **a.** $5.18 - 3.65 =$ _____        **b.** $11.2 - 3.9 =$ _____

    **c.** $16.86 + 9.24 =$ _____       **d.** $0.87 + 0.94 =$ _____

SRB<br/>32-35

# Measuring Length with Metric Units

Your teacher will assign you several objects or distances to measure. Measure each to the nearest centimeter. Then compare your measurements with your partner's. If you do not agree, work together to measure the object again. Record the results in the table.

| Object or Distance | My Measurement | Partner's Measurement | Agreed Measurement |
|---|---|---|---|
| | About _____ cm | About _____ cm | About _____ cm |
| | About _____ cm | About _____ cm | About _____ cm |
| | About _____ cm | About _____ cm | About _____ cm |
| | About _____ cm | About _____ cm | About _____ cm |
| | About _____ cm | About _____ cm | About _____ cm |

## Number Lines

Fill in the missing numbers.

1.

2.

3.

4.

Use with Lesson 4.7.

# Math Boxes 4.7

**1.** Solve.

a.
```
      24
      80
     360
 + 1,200
```
b.
```
       6
     180
      40
 + 1,200
```

**2.** Complete the multiplication and division facts.

a. 5 * _____ = 25

b. 24 ÷ _____ = 4

c. _____ ÷ 7 = 5

d. _____ * 10 = 90

e. 9 * _____ = 36

**3.** Solve each open sentence.

a. 5.6 + K = 10          K = _____

b. 9.09 + S = 13.64      S = _____

c. R − 0.03 = 1.65       R = _____

d. 0.8 − M = 0.6         M = _____

e. F + 1.25 = 12.90      F = _____

**4.** Add 6 tens, 4 hundredths, and 2 tenths to 367.53.

What is the result? _____

**5.** Write as dollars and cents.

a. 25 dimes = $_____._____

b. 40 nickels = $_____._____

c. 15 quarters = $_____._____

d. 40 quarters and 3 dimes =

   $_____._____

**6.** Make up a set of 7 numbers having the following landmarks:

mode: 21

median: 24

maximum: 35

range: 20

____, ____, ____, ____, ____, ____, ____

# Personal References for Units of Length

## Personal References for Metric Units of Length

Use a ruler, meterstick, or tape measure to find common objects that have lengths of 1 centimeter, 1 decimeter, and 1 meter. The lengths do not have to be exact, but they should be close. Ask a friend to look for references with you. You can find more than one reference for each unit. Record the references in the table below.

| Unit of Measure | Personal References |
|---|---|
| 1 centimeter (cm) | |
| 1 decimeter (dm), or 10 centimeters | |
| 1 meter (m) | |

**To be completed in Lesson 5.1.**

## Personal References for U.S. Customary Units of Length

Use a ruler, yardstick, or tape measure to find common objects that have lengths of 1 inch, 1 foot, and 1 yard. The lengths do not have to be exact, but they should be close. Ask a friend to look for references with you. You can find more than one reference for each unit. Record the references in the table below.

| Unit of Measure | Personal References |
|---|---|
| 1 inch (in.) | |
| 1 foot (ft) | |
| 1 yard (yd) | |

**100**

# My Measurement Collection for Metric Units of Length

Use your personal references to estimate the length of an object or a distance in centimeters, decimeters, or meters. Describe the object or distance and record your estimate in the table below. Then measure the object or distance and record the actual measurement in the table.

| Object or Distance | Estimated Length | Actual Length |
| --- | --- | --- |
| | | |
| | | |
| | | |
| | | |
| | | |
| | | |
| | | |
| | | |
| | | |
| | | |
| | | |
| | | |
| | | |
| | | |

Use with Lesson 4.8.

## Math Boxes 4.8

---

**1.  a.** Is 47 closer to 40 or 50?

_____

    **b.** Name the number halfway between

        30 and 40. _____

**2.** Without measuring, estimate the length of your foot, from heel to toe. Then measure the length of your foot.

    **a.** Estimate: About _____ cm

    **b.** Measurement: About _____ cm

---

**3.** Complete.

    **a.** 1 cm = _____ mm

    **b.** 5 cm = _____ mm

    **c.** _____ cm = 30 mm

    **d.** 100 cm = _____ m

    **e.** 200 cm = _____ m

    **f.** 1 m = _____ mm

**4.** Add or subtract.

    **a.** $\begin{array}{r} 309 \\ + \ 721 \\ \hline \end{array}$     **b.** $\begin{array}{r} 700 \\ - \ 299 \\ \hline \end{array}$

---

**5.** Tell whether each number sentence is true or false.

    **a.** $8.77 - 0.08 = 8.50$   _____

    **b.** $35.7 + 22.1 = 57.87$   _____

    **c.** $90.2 - 44.9 < 45$   _____

    **d.** $4.66 + 2.13 > 6$   _____

**6.** Solve the riddle.

I am a polygon.

All my angles have equal measures.

All my sides have equal measures.

What am I? _____

---

Use with Lesson 4.8.

# Measuring in Millimeters

**Math Message**

On your centimeter ruler, the numbered marks are for centimeters and the little marks between centimeter marks are for millimeters.

1.  Look at your centimeter ruler. How many millimeters are in 1 centimeter? _____ mm

2.  Name something that measures about 1 millimeter. _____

    _____

    _____

3.  Draw a line segment that is 8 centimeters long.

4.  Draw a second line segment that is 80 millimeters long.

_____

Measure each line segment below, using both the millimeter side and the centimeter side of the cm/mm ruler. Record both measurements.

5.  A                                                                                    B
    _____

    Length of $\overline{AB}$ = _____ mm = _____ cm

6.  C                                                    D    Length of $\overline{CD}$ = _____ mm = _____ cm
    _____

7.  E   F      Length of $\overline{EF}$ = _____ mm = _____ cm
    ___

_____

**Measuring Land Invertebrates**

An **invertebrate** is an animal that does not have a backbone. (The backbone is also called the spinal column.) Some invertebrates live on land, others in the water. The most common land invertebrates are insects.

The invertebrates shown on page 104, except the earthworm, bumblebee, and mealybug, have been drawn to about actual size. The earthworm can grow to about 4 times the length shown. The bumblebee is shown about twice its actual size and the mealybug about 3 times its actual size.

# Measuring Land Invertebrates (cont.)

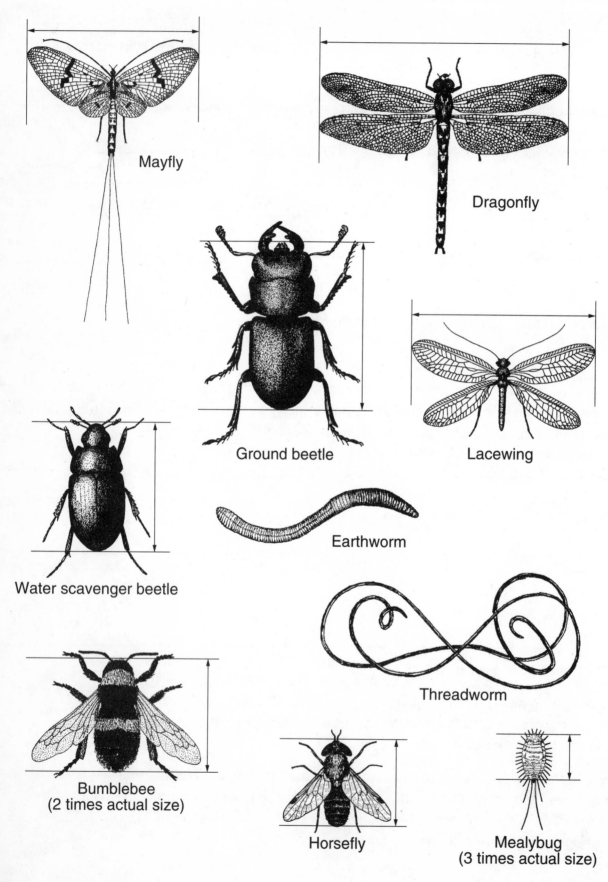

Mayfly

Dragonfly

Ground beetle

Lacewing

Water scavenger beetle

Earthworm

Threadworm

Bumblebee
(2 times actual size)

Horsefly

Mealybug
(3 times actual size)

# Measuring Land Invertebrates (cont.)

Refer to the pictures on page 104
to answer the following questions.

| 1 centimeter (cm) = 10 millimeters (mm) |
|---|
| 1 millimeter = 0.1 centimeter |

1. Measure the following invertebrates to the nearest millimeter by finding the distance between the two guidelines. Then give the lengths in centimeters.

| | | | |
|---|---|---|---|
| **a.** mayfly | About _____ mm | About _____ cm |
| **b.** dragonfly | About _____ mm | About _____ cm |
| **c.** water scavenger beetle | About _____ mm | About _____ cm |
| **d.** ground beetle | About _____ mm | About _____ cm |
| **e.** lacewing | About _____ mm | About _____ cm |
| **f.** horsefly | About _____ mm | About _____ cm |

2. How much longer is the ground beetle than the water scavenger beetle? About _____ cm

3. The bee has been drawn to twice its actual size. In reality, which is longer, the bee

   or the horsefly? _____ How much longer? About _____ mm

4. The mealybug has been drawn to 3 times its
   actual size. In the space at the right, draw
   a mealybug that is about the actual size.

5. What is the actual size of the mealybug in millimeters? _____ mm

6. When straight, the threadworm in the drawing is 306 millimeters long.

   What is its length in centimeters? _____ cm     In meters? _____ m

# Math Boxes 4.9

---

**1.** Write the following numbers using digits:

   **a.** four hundred eighty-two thousand, one

   hundred ninety-seven _____

   **b.** eight hundred million, twelve thousand,

   five _____

---

**2. a.** Measure the length of this line segment to the nearest centimeter.

   _____

   About _____ cm

   **b.** Draw a line segment 7 centimeters long.

---

**3.** Put these numbers in order from smallest to largest.

   1.68     0.78     6.71     6.78     0.61

   _____ _____ _____ _____ , _____

---

**4.** The great spotted kiwi bird is about 114.3 centimeters tall. The greater rhea is about 137.1 centimeters tall. How much taller is the greater rhea than the great spotted kiwi bird?

   _____ centimeters

---

**5.** Add or subtract.

   **a.** $2.46 - 1.34 =$ _____       **b.** $9.6 - 4.8 =$ _____

   **c.** $12.63 + 5.66 =$ _____     **d.** $0.64 + 0.47 =$ _____

Use with Lesson 4.9.

# Place-Value Number Lines

Fill in the missing numbers.

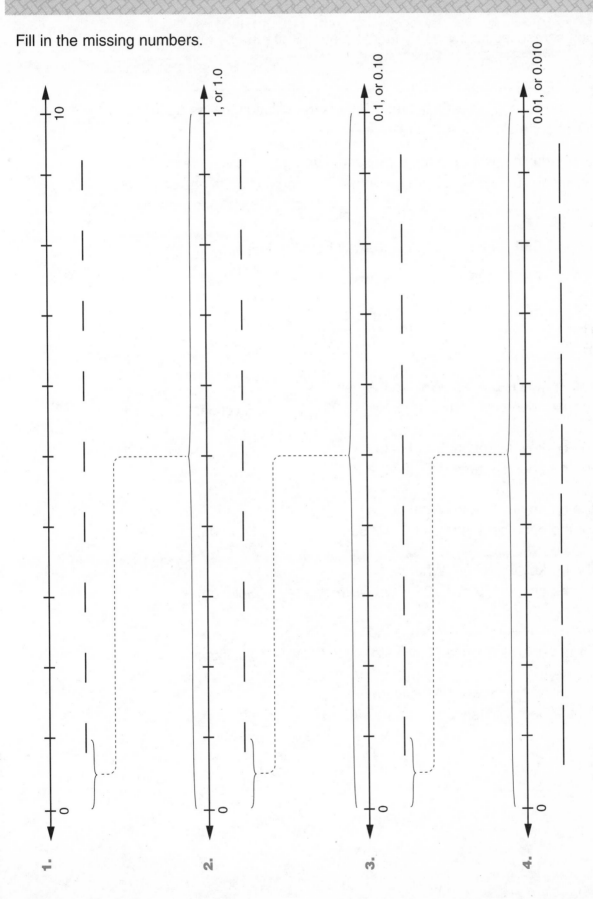

1.    2.    3.    4.

# Broken-Calculator Problems

Solve the open sentences below with your calculator. Pretend one of the calculator keys is broken.

---

***Example*** Pretend the ⊖ key is broken. What is the solution for the open sentence 275 + x = 921?

Replace the variable x with a number and see if you get a true sentence. If it is not true, try other numbers until you get a true sentence. Here is one solution:

Try 700:  275 + **700** = 975          700 is too big.

Try 650:  275 + **650** = 925          Only 4 away from the solution.

Try 654:  275 + **654** = 929          Wrong way!

Try 646:  275 + **646** = 921          This is a true sentence.
                                        646 is the solution.

---

1. Pretend the ⊖ key is broken. What is the
   solution for the open sentence y + 481 = 1,106?          Solution: _____

2. Pretend the ⊕ key is broken. What is the
   solution for the open sentence d − 396 = 235?          Solution: _____

3. Pretend the ⊘ key is broken. What is the
   solution for the open sentence t * 52 = 3,536?          Solution: _____

4. Pretend the ⊖ key is broken. What is the
   solution for the open sentence 12.6 + m = 39.1?          Solution: _____

5. Pretend the ⊕ key is broken. What is the
   solution for the open sentence 30.46 − p = 13.72?          Solution: _____

6. Pretend the ⊕ key is broken. What is the
   solution for the open sentence y − 20.2 = 75.13?          Solution: _____

# Math Boxes 4.10

---

**1. a.** Is 326 closer to 300 or 400?

_____

**b.** Name the number halfway between

500 and 800. _____

---

**2.** Without measuring, estimate the height of your chair. Then measure it.

**a.** Estimate: About _____ cm

**b.** Measurement: About _____ cm

---

**3.** Complete.

**a.** 3 cm = _____ mm

**b.** 15 cm = _____ mm

**c.** _____ cm = 40 mm

**d.** _____ cm = 3 m

**e.** 500 cm = _____ m

**f.** 2 m = _____ mm

---

**4.** Add or subtract.

**a.**    647
      $+\ 228$

**b.**    500
      $-\ 398$

---

**5.** Tell whether each number sentence is true or false.

**a.** $2.34 - 0.09 = 2.25$ _____

**b.** $89.6 + 21.7 = 111.3$ _____

**c.** $56.4 - 23.8 < 33$ _____

**d.** $5.17 + 3.86 > 10$ _____

---

**6.** Name two properties of a regular polygon.

**a.** _____

_____

**b.** _____

_____

---

## Time to Reflect

1. Apart from math class, describe two times when you have used decimals. Or, if you have not used decimals, describe two times when you could have used them.

   _____

   _____

   _____

   _____

   _____

   _____

2. What was the easiest lesson in this unit? Why was it easy?

   _____

   _____

   _____

   _____

   _____

   _____

3. What was the hardest lesson in this unit? What strategies did you use to try to understand it better?

   _____

   _____

   _____

   _____

   _____

   _____

# Math Boxes 4.11

---

**1.** Which of the following is closest to the sum of 721, 2,876, and 15,103?

5,000

10,000

15,000

20,000

---

**2.** Complete.

**a.** 4 * 8 = _____

**b.** 4 * 80 = _____

**c.** _____ = 5 * 3

**d.** _____ = 50 * 3

**e.** 6 * 6 = _____

**f.** 6 * 60 = _____

---

**3.** **a.** Is 63 closer to 60 or 70?

_____

**b.** Name the number halfway between 80 and 90. _____

**c.** Is 572 closer to 500 or 600? _____

**d.** Name the number halfway between 300 and 600. _____

---

**4.** Write the following numbers using digits:

**a.** one million, three hundred forty-six thousand, thirteen

_____

**b.** twenty-two million, fifteen thousand, three hundred fifty-four

_____

---

**5.**

| **a.** | | **b.** | | **c.** | | **d.** | |
|---|---|---|---|---|---|---|---|
| | 35 | | 18 | | 54 | | 48 |
| | 100 | | 420 | | 180 | | 720 |
| | 280 | | 120 | | 360 | | 180 |
| + | 800 | + | 2,800 | + | 1,200 | + | 2,700 |

---

# Multiplying Ones by Tens

You can extend a multiplication fact by making one of the factors a multiple of ten.

*Example*

Original fact: 2 * 3 = 6

Extended facts: 2 * **30** = _____ , or **20** * 3 = _____

Write a multiplication fact for each Fact Triangle shown below.
Then extend this fact by changing one of the factors to a multiple of ten.

**1.**

Original fact: ____6 * 8 = 48____

Extended fact: ____6 * 80 =____

**2.**

Original fact: _____

Extended fact: _____

**3.**

Original fact: _____

Extended fact: _____

**4.**

Original fact: _____

Extended fact: _____

**5.** What shortcut can you use to multiply ones by tens, such as 3 * 60?

_____

_____

Use with Lesson 5.1.

# Multiplying Tens by Tens

You can extend a multiplication fact by making both factors multiples of ten.

*Example*

Original fact: 3 * 5 = 15

Extended fact: **30** * **50** = _____

Write a multiplication fact for each Fact Triangle shown below.
Then extend this fact by changing both factors to multiples of ten.

**1.**

Original fact: _____4 * 6 = 24_____

Extended fact: _____40 * 60 =_____

**2.**

Original fact: _____

Extended fact: _____

**3.**

Original fact: _____

Extended fact: _____

**4.**

Original fact: _____

Extended fact: _____

**5.** What shortcut can you use to multiply tens by tens, such as 40 * 60?

_____

_____

# Math Boxes 5.1

---

**1.** Five children share 27 tennis balls equally.

Each child gets _____ balls.

There are _____ balls left over.

---

**2.** A number has

6 in the tenths place,
9 in the hundreds place,
2 in the thousands place,
7 in the ones place,
3 in the tens place, and
5 in the hundredths place.

Write the number.

____ , ____ ____ ____ . ____ ____

SRB
29

---

**3.** Complete.

a. $40 * 50 =$ _____

b. $70 * 300 =$ _____

c. $60 *$ _____ $= 180$

d. _____ $* 9 = 7,200$

e. $90 *$ _____ $= 810$

SRB
16

---

**4.** Add.

a.
```
   4,500
     540
     100
+     12
```

b.
```
      18
     420
      90
+  2,100
```

SRB
9 10

---

**5.** Measure each line segment to the nearest $\frac{1}{4}$ inch.

a.
  G                                     H

About _____ inches

b. _____
  B                                            Y

About _____ inches

SRB
108

---

Use with Lesson 5.1.

## Multiplication Wrestling Worksheet

**Round 1**   Cards: _____  _____  _____  _____

Numbers formed: _____ * _____

Teams: (_____ + _____) * (_____ + _____)

Products: _____ * _____ = _____

_____ * _____ = _____

_____ * _____ = _____

_____ * _____ = _____

Total (add 4 products): _____

---

**Round 2**   Cards: _____  _____  _____  _____

Numbers formed: _____ * _____

Teams: (_____ + _____) * (_____ + _____)

Products: _____ * _____ = _____

_____ * _____ = _____

_____ * _____ = _____

_____ * _____ = _____

Total (add 4 products): _____

---

**Round 3**   Cards: _____  _____  _____  _____

Numbers formed: _____ * _____

Teams: (_____ + _____) * (_____ + _____)

Products: _____ * _____ = _____

_____ * _____ = _____

_____ * _____ = _____

_____ * _____ = _____

Total (add 4 products): _____

# Place Value in Decimals

**1.** Write these numbers in order from smallest to largest.

    1.26     0.58     1.09     1.091     0.35

_____

_____

_____

_____

_____

**2.** A number has

6 in the tenths place,
4 in the ones place,
5 in the hundredths place, and
9 in the tens place.

Write the number.

\_\_\_\_ \_\_\_\_ . \_\_\_\_ \_\_\_\_

**3.** Write the smallest number you can make with the following digits:

    3     6     4     7     2

_____

**4.** What is the value of the digit 4 in the numerals below?

**a.** 37.48 _____

**b.** 49.08 _____

**c.** 0.942 _____

**d.** 1.664 _____

**5.** Write each number using digits.

**a.** four and seventy-two hundredths

_____

**b.** nine hundred thirty-five thousandths

_____

**6.** I am a four-digit number less than 10.

• The digit in the tenths place is the result of dividing 36 by 4.

• The digit in the hundredths place is the result of dividing 42 by 7.

• The digit in the ones place is the result of dividing 72 by 8.

• The digit in the thousandths place is the result of dividing 35 by 5.

What number am I?

\_\_\_\_ . \_\_\_\_ \_\_\_\_ \_\_\_\_

                                             Use with Lesson 5.2.

# Math Boxes 5.2

---

**1.** Divide.

   **a.** 45 / 9 = _____

   **b.** 450 / 90 = _____

   **c.** 1,000 / 200 = _____

   **d.** _____ = 2,000 / 40

   **e.** _____ = 6,300 / 700

SRB
20

---

**2.** Measure the line segment to the nearest millimeter. Record the measurement in millimeters and centimeters.

_____

   **a.** _____ mm

   **b.** _____ cm _____ mm

SRB
108

---

**3.** Tell whether each number sentence is true or false.

   **a.** (4.6 + 2.9) − 3.1 < 3.7 _____

   **b.** 0.20 > 0.68 − (0.42 + 0.11) _____

   **c.** 7.89 − 3.36 = 4.53 _____

   **d.** 12.6 − 4.8 = 3.9 + 3.9 _____

SRB
32-35
128

---

**4.** Write > or < to make each a true number sentence.

   **a.** 4,500,999 _____ 879,662

   **b.** 23,468,000 _____ 23,467,000

   **c.** 568,009,352 _____ 568,010,320

   **d.** 400,632 _____ 399,800

SRB
6  128

---

**5.** Fill in the missing numbers on each number line.

   **a.**

      0.20                                                         0.30

   **b.**

      2.6                                 2.67               2.7

---

# Planning a Driving Trip

**Math Message**

The airline you are using on the World
Tour will give you a $200 discount coupon
for every 15,000 miles you fly. Suppose
you have flown the distances shown in the
table at the right.

Have you flown enough miles
to get a discount coupon? _____

| | |
|---|---|
| Washington, D.C. → Cairo | 5,980 mi |
| Cairo → Accra | 2,420 mi |
| Accra → Cairo | 2,420 mi |
| Cairo → Budapest | 1,380 mi |
| Budapest → London | 1,040 mi |

Use the map on journal page 119. Start at your hometown. Plan a driving trip that
takes you to 4 other cities on the map. If your hometown is not on the map, find the
nearest city on the map to your hometown. Start your driving trip from this city.

*Example Trip*   Start in Chicago. Drive to St. Louis, Louisville,
Birmingham, and then New Orleans.

You plan to drive about 8 hours a day and then stop for the night. You want to find
out how many **days** this driving trip will take.

1. Record your routes, driving distances, and driving times in the table.

| From...To | Driving Distance (miles) | Driving Time (hours:minutes) | Rounded Time (hours) |
|---|---|---|---|
| | ___ ___ ___ | ___:___ ___ | ___ |
| | ___ ___ ___ | ___:___ ___ | ___ |
| | ___ ___ ___ | ___:___ ___ | ___ |
| | ___ ___ ___ | ___:___ ___ | ___ |

2. Estimate how many **miles** in all you will drive.   About _____ miles

3. Estimate how many **hours** in all you will drive.   About _____ hours

4. Tell how many days it will take to complete the trip.   _____ days

Date _____  Time _____

# Estimated U.S. Distances and Driving Times

*Example*

San Francisco •———— 384 ————• Los Angeles
                        7:15

384 is the distance in miles
7:15 is the driving time (hours:minutes)

Use with Lesson 5.3.

# Logic Problems

1. Theresa, Keiko, Jamal, and Mario live in Lansing, Michigan. Each has a favorite season. No two of them like the same season.

   • Theresa likes to go to the beach.

   • Keiko doesn't like snow.

   • Jamal doesn't like spring flowers.

   • Mario likes to go skiing.

   What is each person's favorite season? You may use a logic grid to help you.

|  | **Winter** | **Spring** | **Summer** | **Fall** |
|---|---|---|---|---|
| Keiko |  |  |  |  |
| Jamal |  |  |  |  |
| Theresa |  |  |  |  |
| Mario |  |  |  |  |

Keiko _____       Jamal _____

Theresa _____       Mario _____

2. Lynn, Julie, Elaine, and Pierre each have a favorite pizza. No two of them like the same topping. They ordered one of each of the following: shrimp, sausage, cheese, and spinach.

   • Lynn is a vegetarian and will not eat meat or seafood.

   • Pierre is allergic to seafood.

   • Elaine likes meat toppings, but not seafood.

   • Neither Pierre nor Julie likes vegetables.

   What kind of pizza did each person eat?

Lynn _____       Pierre _____

Elaine _____       Julie _____

## Math Boxes 5.3

**1.** Sara collected 30 leaves. On the way to school, she lost 2 of them. At school, she shared them equally with her 6 friends. How many leaves did each friend get?

_____ leaves

**2.** A number has

2 in the hundreds place,
7 in the tenths place,
6 in the hundredths place,
4 in the ones place,
5 in the tens place, and
1 in the thousandths place.

Write the number.

____ ____ ____ . ____ ____ ____

**3.** Complete.

a. $3 * 40 =$ _____

b. $90 * 70 =$ _____

c. $50 *$ _____ $= 3,000$

d. _____ $* 8 = 1,600$

e. $80 *$ _____ $= 56,000$

**4.** Add.

a.
```
     72
    450
    160
+ 1,000
```

b.
```
     15
    240
    350
+ 5,600
```

**5.** Measure each line segment to the nearest $\frac{1}{4}$ inch.

a.

E                                                                    R

About _____ inches

b.

L                                        Y

About _____ inches

# What Do Americans Eat?

Several years ago, the U.S. Department of Agriculture conducted a survey to find out how much food Americans eat. In the survey, a large number of people were asked to keep lists of all the foods they ate for several days.

These lists were then used to estimate how much of each food is eaten during one year. The "average" American eats about 1,431 pounds of food per year. This is about 4 pounds of food per day.

This survey found that the average American eats or drinks about the following amounts in one year:

| | |
|---|---|
| 2 | pounds of broccoli |
| 4 | pounds of potato chips |
| 7 | pounds of peanuts |
| 18 | pounds of candy |
| 27 | pounds of lettuce |
| 44 | gallons of soft drinks |
| 80 | hot dogs |
| 89 | pounds of fresh fruit |
| 121 | pounds of potatoes |
| 176 | glasses of fruit juice |
| 200 | hamburgers |
| 255 | eggs |
| 752 | glasses of water |

Use your answers to the Math Message question to complete these statements.

1. I will drink about _____ glasses of fruit juice in one year.

2. I will eat about _____ hot dogs in one year.

3. I will eat about _____ hamburgers in one year.

# Estimating Averages

- **Estimate** whether the answer will be in the tens, hundreds, thousands, or more.
- Write a number model to show how you estimated.
- Then circle the box that shows your estimate.

*Example* Alice sleeps an average of 9 hours a night. How many hours does she sleep in one year?

Number model  $\underline{10 * 400 = 4,000}$

| 10s | 100s | (1,000s) | 10,000s | 100,000s | 1,000,000s |
|-----|------|----------|---------|----------|------------|

1. An average of about 23 new species of insects are discovered each day. About how many new species are discovered in one year?

   Number model _____

| 10s | 100s | 1,000s | 10,000s | 100,000s | 1,000,000s |
|-----|------|--------|---------|----------|------------|

2. A housefly beats its wings about 190 times per second. That's about how many times per minute?

   Number model _____

| 10s | 100s | 1,000s | 10,000s | 100,000s | 1,000,000s |
|-----|------|--------|---------|----------|------------|

3. A blue whale weighs about as much as 425,000 kittens. About how many kittens weigh as much as 4 blue whales?

   Number model _____

| 10s | 100s | 1,000s | 10,000s | 100,000s | 1,000,000s |
|-----|------|--------|---------|----------|------------|

4. An average bee can lift about 300 times its own weight. If a 170-pound person were as strong as a bee, about how many pounds could this person lift?

   Number model _____

| 10s | 100s | 1,000s | 10,000s | 100,000s | 1,000,000s |
|-----|------|--------|---------|----------|------------|

# Math Boxes 5.4

---

**1.** Divide.

   **a.** 18,000 / 9 = _____

   **b.** 350 / 7 = _____

   **c.** 3,500 / 5 = _____

   **d.** _____ = 42,000 / 60

   **e.** _____ = 5,600 / 800

**2.** Measure the line segment to the nearest millimeter. Record the measurement in millimeters and centimeters.

   _____

   **a.** _____ mm

   **b.** _____ cm _____ mm

---

**3.** Tell whether each number sentence is true or false.

   **a.** $(7.6 + 3.8) - 5.2 < 5.9$ _____

   **b.** $0.50 > 1.43 - (0.77 + 0.19)$ _____

   **c.** $14.66 - 12.09 = 3.46$ _____

   **d.** $15.8 - 11.9 = 1.6 + 2.7$ _____

**4.** Write $>$ or $<$ to make each a true number sentence.

   **a.** 9,000,000 _____ 8,999,999

   **b.** 421,936,500 _____ 422,985,600

   **c.** 68,004,002 _____ 68,004,100

   **d.** 600,523 _____ 601,000

---

**5.** Fill in the missing numbers on each number line.

   **a.**

    5.0                                                      6.0

   **b.**

    4.73                                      5.43         5.73

---

Use with Lesson 5.4.

## The Partial-Products Method

1. Multiply. Show your work in the grid below.

   a.  59 * 6 = _____

   b.  _____ = 3 * 470

   c.  2 * 1,523 = _____

Example   6 * 463 = ?

```
1,000s |100s|10s| 1s
       |  4 | 6 | 3
  *    |    |   | 6
  ─────────────────
  2 |  4 | 0 | 0  ← 6 [400s]
     |  3 | 6 | 0  ← 6 [60s]
  +  |    | 1 | 8  ← 6 [3s]
  ─────────────────
  2 |  7 | 7 | 8
```

2. On an "average" day, about 217 pairs of
   twins are born in the United States.
   About how many pairs of twins are born
   in 1 week?

   a.  **Estimate** whether the answer will be in the tens, hundreds, thousands,
       or more. Circle the box that shows your estimate.

   | 10s | 100s | 1,000s | 10,000s | 100,000s | 1,000,000s |
   |-----|------|--------|---------|----------|------------|

   b.  **Calculate** the answer in the grid below.        About _____ pairs of twins

# My Measurement Collection for Units of Length

Use your personal references on journal page 100 to estimate the length or height of an object or distance in inches, feet, or yards. Describe the object or distance and record your estimate in the table below. Then measure the object or distance and record the actual measurement in the table.

| Object or Distance | Estimated Length | Actual Length |
|---|---|---|
|  |  |  |
|  |  |  |
|  |  |  |
|  |  |  |
|  |  |  |
|  |  |  |
|  |  |  |
|  |  |  |
|  |  |  |
|  |  |  |
|  |  |  |
|  |  |  |
|  |  |  |
|  |  |  |
|  |  |  |
|  |  |  |

Use with Lesson 5.5.

# Math Boxes 5.5

**1.** Look at the grid below.

          A   B   C

**a.** In which column is the circle located?

_____

**b.** In which row is the circle located?

_____

**2.** Write each number using digits.

**a.** five million, two hundred sixty-eight thousand, four

_____

**b.** two hundred million, three thousand, eighty-eight

_____

**3.** Circle the number that is closest to the sum of 387, 945, and 1,024.

1,600

2,000

2,400

2,800

**4.** Multiply. Use the partial-products method.

$9 * 237 =$ _____

**5.** Carlos, Frank, Mia, and Lauren each have a different favorite fruit: apples, grapes, watermelon, or peaches.

• Carlos likes a fruit that has a large seed in it.

• Mia likes a smaller fruit that is usually green or red.

• Lauren does not like watermelon or grapes.

Which fruit does each student like best?

Lauren _____    Mia _____

Carlos _____    Frank _____

# Multiplication Number Stories

Follow these steps for each problem.

    **a.** Decide which two numbers need to be multiplied to give the exact answer. Write the two numbers.

    **b.** Estimate whether the answer will be in the tens, hundreds, thousands, or more. Write a number model for the estimate. Circle the box to show your estimate.

    **c.** On the grid below, find the exact answer by multiplying the two numbers. Write the answer.

1. The average person drinks about 15 glasses of milk a month. About how many glasses of milk is that per year?

    **a.** _____ * _____     **b.** _____     **c.** _____

       numbers that will give               number model for your              exact answer
       the exact answer                    estimate

| 10s | 100s | 1,000s | 10,000s | 100,000s | 1,000,000s |
|-----|------|--------|---------|----------|------------|

2. Eighteen newborn hummingbirds weigh about 1 ounce. About how many of them does it take to make 1 pound? (1 pound = 16 ounces)

    **a.** _____ * _____     **b.** _____     **c.** _____

       numbers that will give               number model for your              exact answer
       the exact answer                    estimate

| 10s | 100s | 1,000s | 10,000s | 100,000s | 1,000,000s |
|-----|------|--------|---------|----------|------------|

Use with Lesson 5.6.

## Multiplication Number Stories (cont.)

3. A test found that a lightbulb lasts an average of 63 days after being turned on. About how many hours is that?

a. _____ * _____

numbers that will give
the exact answer

b. _____

number model for your
estimate

c. _____

exact answer

| 10s | 100s | 1,000s | 10,000s | 100,000s | 1,000,000s |
|-----|------|--------|---------|----------|------------|

4. A full-grown oak tree loses an average of about 7 tons of water through its leaves per day. About how many tons of water is that per year?

a. _____ * _____

numbers that will give
the exact answer

b. _____

number model for your
estimate

c. _____

exact answer

| 10s | 100s | 1,000s | 10,000s | 100,000s | 1,000,000s |
|-----|------|--------|---------|----------|------------|

# Math Boxes 5.6

---

**1.** If you remove 7 gallons a day from a 65-gallon water tank, how long will it take to empty the tank?

_____

SRB
149

---

**2.** Write each number using digits.

a. three hundred forty-two thousandths

_____

b. six and twenty-five hundredths

_____

SRB
26 29

---

**3.** Circle the number that is closest to the product of 48 and 21.

10

100

1,000

10,000

SRB
155  156

---

**4.** Multiply. Use the partial-products method.

 = 52 * 23

SRB
17

---

**5.** a. Measure the line segment to the nearest $\frac{1}{4}$ inch.

_____

_____ inches

b. Draw a line segment that is half as long as the one above.

c. How long is the line segment you drew? _____ inches

SRB
108

---

# Lattice Multiplication

**Part A** Use the lattice method to find the products.

**1.** 3 * 56 = _____

5    6

3

**2.** 8 * 26 = _____

2    6

8

**3.** 7 * 74 = _____

**4.** 6 * 315 = _____

**5.** 9 * 284 = _____

**Part B** Use the lattice method to find the products.

**6.** 47 * 63 = _____

6    3

4

7

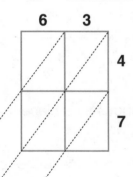

**7.** 26 * 26 = _____

**8.** 16 * 473 = _____

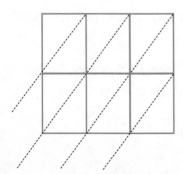

**9.** 46 * 805 = _____

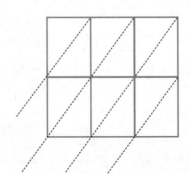

# Place Value in Whole Numbers

1. Write these numbers in order from smallest to largest.

   964   9,460   96,400   400,960   94,600

   _____

   _____

   _____

   _____

   _____

2. A number has

   5 in the hundreds place,
   7 in the ten-thousands place,
   0 in the ones place,
   9 in the thousands place, and
   8 in the tens place.

   Write the number.

   _____ _____ , _____ _____ _____

3. Write the largest number you can make with the following digits:

   3   5   0   7   9   2

   _____

4. What is the value of the digit 8 in the numerals below?

   a. 807,941 _____

   b. 583 _____

   c. 8,714 _____

   d. 86,490 _____

5. Write each number using digits.

   a. four hundred eighty-seven thousand, sixty-three

      _____

   b. fifteen thousand, two hundred ninety-seven

      _____

6. I am a 5-digit number.

   • The digit in the thousands place is the result of dividing 64 by 8.

   • The digit in the ones place is the result of dividing 63 by 9.

   • The digit in the ten-thousands place is the result of dividing 54 by 6.

   • The digit in the tens place is the result of dividing 40 by 5.

   • The digit in the hundreds place is the result of dividing 33 by 11.

   What number am I?

   _____ _____ , _____ _____ _____

Use with Lesson 5.7.

# Math Boxes 5.7

---

**1.** Look at the grid below.

   **a.** In which column is the triangle located?

   _____

   **b.** In which row is the triangle located?

   _____

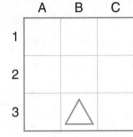

**2.** Write each number using digits.

   **a.** twenty-six million, nineteen thousand, eighteen

   _____

   **b.** three hundred fifty-two million, eight hundred thousand, two hundred

   _____

---

**3.** Circle the number that is closest to the sum of 715, 1,904, and 688.

   3,000

   3,300

   3,600

   3,900

**4.** Multiply. Use the partial-products method.

   $6 * 509 =$ _____

---

**5.** Matthew, Mark, Elizabeth, and John each have a different favorite kind of book: mystery, science fiction, biography, or historical fiction.

- Matthew likes books with lots of clues.

- John likes books about events that might take place in the future.

- Elizabeth does not like to read about anything that didn't really happen.

Which kind of book does each student like best?

Matthew _____     Elizabeth _____

Mark _____     John _____

---

# Reading and Writing Big Numbers

1. Each row in the place-value chart shows a number. Write the name for each number below the chart.

|  | Billions | | | | Millions | | | | Thousands | | | | Ones | | |
|---|---|---|---|---|---|---|---|---|---|---|---|---|---|---|---|
|  | 100B | 10B | 1B | , | 100M | 10M | 1M | , | 100Th | 10Th | 1Th | , | 100 | 10 | 1 |
| a. |  |  | 7 | , | 4 | 0 | 0 | , | 0 | 6 | 5 | , | 2 | 0 | 0 |
| b. |  |  |  |  |  | 5 | 1 | , | 8 | 0 | 0 | , | 0 | 0 | 0 |
| c. |  | 2 | 3 | , | 0 | 0 | 0 | , | 0 | 0 | 5 | , | 1 | 4 | 0 |
| d. | 1 | 2 | 3 | , | 4 | 5 | 6 | , | 7 | 8 | 9 | , | 0 | 1 | 2 |

a. _7 billion, 400 million, 65 thousand, 200_

b. _____

c. _____

d. _____

2. Write these numbers in the place-value chart below.

a. 400 thousand, 500

b. 208 million, 350 thousand, 600

c. 16 billion, 210 million, 48 thousand, 715

d. 1 billion, 1 million, 1 thousand, 1

|  | Billions | | | | Millions | | | | Thousands | | | | Ones | | |
|---|---|---|---|---|---|---|---|---|---|---|---|---|---|---|---|
|  | 100B | 10B | 1B | , | 100M | 10M | 1M | , | 100Th | 10Th | 1Th | , | 100 | 10 | 1 |
| a. |  |  |  |  |  |  |  |  |  |  |  |  |  |  |  |
| b. |  |  |  |  |  |  |  |  |  |  |  |  |  |  |  |
| c. |  |  |  |  |  |  |  |  |  |  |  |  |  |  |  |
| d. |  |  |  |  |  |  |  |  |  |  |  |  |  |  |  |

Use with Lesson 5.8.

# How Much Are a Million and a Billion?

1. How many dots are on the 50 by 40 array page? _____ dots

2. How many dots would be on

   a. 5 pages?     _____ dots

   b. 50 pages?     _____ dots

   c. 500 pages?     _____ dots

3. Each package of paper, or ream, contains 500 sheets. How many dots would be on the paper in

   a. 1 ream? (*Hint:* Look at Problem 2.)     _____ dots

   b. 10 reams? (1 carton)     _____ dots

   c. 100 reams? (10 cartons)     _____ dots

   d. 1,000 reams? (100 cartons)     _____ dots

4. Write these numbers in the place-value chart below.

   a. 999 thousand     b. 1,000 thousand     c. 999 million     d. 1,000 million

|   | Billions | | | | Millions | | | | Thousands | | | | Ones | | |
|---|------|-----|----|---|------|-----|----|---|-------|------|-----|---|-----|----|---|
|   | 100B | 10B | 1B | , | 100M | 10M | 1M | , | 100Th | 10Th | 1Th | , | 100 | 10 | 1 |
| a. | | | | | | | | | | | | | | | |
| b. | | | | | | | | | | | | | | | |
| c. | | | | | | | | | | | | | | | |
| d. | | | | | | | | | | | | | | | |

# Math Boxes 5.8

---

**1.** You have 75 cookies. You give 8 cookies to each of your friends until you run out of cookies.

   **a.** How many friends will get 8 cookies? _____

   **b.** How many cookies will you get if you keep the rest for yourself? _____

**2.** Write each number using digits.

   **a.** seven hundred six thousandths

   _____

   **b.** three and four hundredths

   _____

---

**3.** Circle the number that is closest to the product of 41 and 83.

   30

   300

   3,000

   30,000

**4.** Multiply. Use the partial-products method.

   _____ = 46 * 98

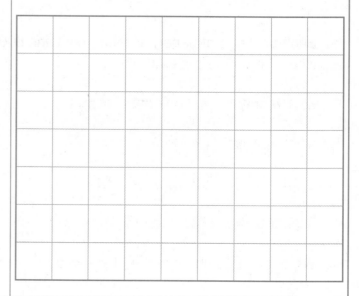

---

**5. a.** Measure the line segment to the nearest $\frac{1}{4}$ inch.

R _____ S

   _____ inches

   **b.** Draw a line segment that is half the length of $\overline{RS}$.

   **c.** How long is the line segment you drew? _____ inches

---

# Place Value and Powers of 10

| | Millions | Hundred-Thousands | Ten-Thousands | Thousands | Hundreds | Tens | Ones |
|---|---|---|---|---|---|---|---|
| 1. | 1,000,000 | | | 1,000 | 100 | | 1 |
| 2. | 10 [100,000s] | | | 10 [100s] | 10 [10s] | | 10 [tenths] |
| 3. | | | 10 * 10 * 10 * 10 | | 10 * 10 | | |
| 4. | | $10^5$ | | $10^3$ | $10^2$ | | $10^0$ |

Fill in this place-value chart as follows:

1. Write standard numbers in Row 1.

2. In Row 2, write the value of each place to show that it is 10 times the value of the place to its right.

3. In Row 3, write the place values as products of 10s.

4. In Row 4, show the values as powers of 10. Use exponents. The exponent shows how many times 10 is used as a factor. It also shows how many zeros are in the standard number.

# Multiplication of Whole Numbers

Use the **partial-products** method to solve Problems 1 and 2.

1.  The school lunchroom purchased
    55 dozen eggs. How many eggs
    were purchased?

    _____ eggs

2.  76 * 59 = _____

Use the **lattice method** to solve Problems 3 and 4.

3.  23 * 314 = _____

4.  An opossum sleeps an average
    of 19 hours per day. How many
    hours does an opossum sleep
    during a 4-week time period?

    _____ hours

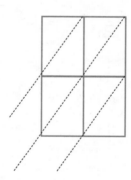

5.  Write a multiplication number story using the numbers 85 and 64. You may use
    the method of your choice to solve it.

    _____

    _____

    _____

    _____

    Answer: _____
    <br>(unit)

Use with Lesson 5.9.

# Math Boxes 5.9

---

**1.** Which of the angles below has a measure of about 90 degrees? Circle it.

SRB
78 79

**2.** Circle the number that is closest to the sum of 1,254, 8,902, and 2,877.

6,000

9,000

12,000

15,000

SRB
155

---

**3.** Write $<$, $>$, or $=$ to make each number sentence true.

**a.** 62 million _____ 3,100,000,000

**b.** $10^3$ _____ 10,000

**c.** 5,800,000 _____ 58 million

**d.** 100,000 _____ $10^6$

SRB
6

**4.** Complete.

**a.** $10^4 =$ _____

**b.** $10^{\square} = 10 * 10 * 10 * 10 * 10$

**c.** $100 = 10^{\square}$

**d.** 10 to the seventh power =

_____

SRB
5

---

**5.** Multiply. Use the lattice method.

**a.** $6 * 347 =$ _____

**b.** _____ $= 9 * 258$

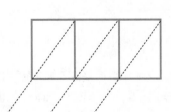

SRB
18

---

# Evaluating Large Numbers

1. Round the attendance figures in the table to the nearest hundred-thousand.

| 1999 Major League Baseball—Attendance of Home Games for 10 Teams | | |
|---|---|---|
| Team | Attendance | Attendance Rounded to the Nearest 100,000 |
| 1. Colorado Rockies | 3,481,065 | |
| 2. Baltimore Orioles | 3,432,099 | |
| 3. Cleveland Indians | 3,468,436 | |
| 4. Los Angeles Dodgers | 3,098,042 | |
| 5. Atlanta Braves | 3,284,901 | |
| 6. Texas Rangers | 2,774,501 | |
| 7. Seattle Mariners | 2,915,908 | |
| 8. St. Louis Cardinals | 3,235,833 | |
| 9. Boston Red Sox | 2,446,277 | |
| 10. New York Yankees | 3,293,659 | |

*Source: Information Please Sports Almanac*

2. How do you think attendance figures for major league baseball games are obtained?

_____

_____

3. Do you think *exactly* 3,481,065 people were at the home games played by the Colorado Rockies? Explain your answer.

_____

_____

4. You rounded the figures in the table above to the nearest hundred-thousand. Which two pairs of teams have the same attendance figures based on these rounded numbers?

_____

_____

# Many Names for Powers of 10

At the bottom of the page, there are different names for powers of 10.
Write each of these names in the appropriate name-collection box.
Compare your answers with your partner's.

**1.**

| 100,000 |
| --- |
|  |
|  |
|  |

**2.**

| $10^2$ |
| --- |
|  |
|  |
|  |

**3.**

| 1 million |
| --- |
|  |
|  |
|  |

**4.**

| one |
| --- |
|  |
|  |
|  |

**5.**

| 10 * 10 * 10 |
| --- |
|  |
|  |
|  |

**6.**

| $10^4$ |
| --- |
|  |
|  |
|  |

**7.**

| 10 [1s] |
| --- |
|  |
|  |
|  |

| | | |
| --- | --- | --- |
| 1,000,000 | 10,000 | 1,000 |
| 100 | 10 | 10 [100,000s] |
| 10 [10,000s] | $10^6$ | 10 [1,000s] |
| $10^3$ | 10 * 10 * 10 * 10 | one thousand |
| $10^5$ | 10 * 10 * 10 * 10 * 10 | 10 [10s] |
| 10 * 10 | ten | $10^1$ |
| 10 [tenths] | $10^0$ | 1 |

# Math Boxes 5.10

**1.** There are 60 trading cards. Each student gets 5 cards. How many students are there?

_____ students

**2.** Write each number using digits.

**a.** eighty-five thousandths

_____

**b.** fourteen and three tenths

_____

**3.** Circle the number that is closest to the product of 37 and 91.

36

360

3,600

36,000

**4.** Multiply. Use the partial-products method.

_____ = 43 * 89

**5. a.** Measure the line segment to the nearest $\frac{1}{4}$ inch.

T _____ G

About _____ inches

**b.** Draw a line segment that is half the length of $\overline{TG}$.

**c.** How long is the line segment you drew? _____ inches

# Traveling to Europe

It is time to leave Africa. Your destination is Region 2—the continent of Europe. You and your classmates will fly from Cairo, Egypt to Budapest, Hungary. Before exploring Hungary, you will collect information about the countries in Region 2. You may even decide to visit another country in Europe after your stay in Budapest.

Use the World Tour section of your *Student Reference Book* to answer the questions. Use the Country Profiles for Region 2 on page 224.

1. Which country in Region 2 has

   a. the largest population?  _____
   
      country                                        population

   b. the smallest population? _____
   
      country                                        population

   c. the largest area?        _____
   
      country                                        area

   d. the smallest area?       _____
   
      country                                        area

Use the Climate and Elevation of Capital Cities table on page 241.

2. From December to February, which capital in Region 2 has

   a. the warmest weather?    _____
   
      capital          country             temperatures

   b. the coolest weather?    _____
   
      capital          country             temperatures

   c. the greatest amount of rain?  _____
   
      capital          country             inches rainfall

   d. the least amount of rain?     _____
   
      capital          country             inches rainfall

Use the Population Data table on page 245.

3. Which country in Region 2 has

   a. the greatest percent of population ages 0–14?  _____
   
      country             percent

   b. the smallest percent of population ages 0–14?  _____
   
      country             percent

# Math Boxes 5.11

---

**1.** Which of the angles below has a measure less than 90 degrees? Circle it.

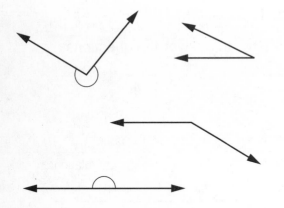

**2.** Circle the number that is closest to the sum of 799, 11,304, and 48,609.

20,000

40,000

60,000

80,000

---

**3.** Write $<$, $>$, or $=$ to make each number sentence true.

a. 100,000 _____ $10^5$

b. 670,000 _____ 67,000,000

c. $10^2$ _____ 1,000

d. 62 billion _____ 9,700,000

**4.** Complete.

a. $10^2 =$ _____

b. $10^{\square} = 10 * 10 * 10 * 10$

c. $1,000 = 10^{\square}$

d. 10 to the ninth power $=$

_____

---

**5.** Multiply. Use the lattice method.

a. $7 * 208 =$ _____

b. _____ $= 9 * 256$

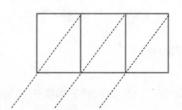

# Time to Reflect

1. During the past few weeks, about how many times did you use estimation outside of school? Describe some of those situations. Or, if you did not estimate, describe two times when you could have estimated.

_____

_____

_____

_____

_____

_____

2. Which of the big number names is the hardest for you to remember? Invent a memory device or method to help you remember how many zeros go after this number. Explain your trick.

_____

_____

_____

_____

_____

_____

3. Do you think multiplication is easy or hard? Explain your answer.

_____

_____

_____

_____

_____

_____

# Math Boxes 5.12

---

**1.** There are 240 chairs to set up for the concert. Each row has 40 chairs in it. How many rows are there?

_____ rows

**2.** The senior class at Rees High School raised $1,895 for five charities in the community. The money will be shared equally. How much money will each charity receive?

_____

---

**3.** Look at the grid below.

**a.** In which column is the star located?

_____

**b.** In which row is the star located?

_____

**4.** Draw a right angle with vertex *K*.

---

**5.** Divide.

**a.** 72 / 9 = _____

**g.** 28 / 4 = _____

**k.** _____ = 24 / 6

**b.** 720 / 90 = _____

**h.** 28,000 / 40 = _____

**l.** _____ = 2,400 / 600

**c.** 7,200 / 900 = _____

**i.** 28,000 / 400 = _____

**m.** _____ = 2,400 / 60

**d.** _____ = 42 / 7

**j.** 2,800 / 400 = _____

**n.** _____ = 24,000 / 6

**e.** _____ = 420 / 7

**f.** _____ = 4,200 / 7

---

# A Multiples-of-10 Strategy for Division

For Problems 1–4, fill in the multiples-of-10 list. Use the completed list to help answer the question. Then write a number model.

1. The refreshment stand sold 276 cans of soda this weekend. How many 6-packs is that?

   10 [6s] = _____

   20 [6s] = _____

   30 [6s] = _____

   40 [6s] = _____

   50 [6s] = _____

   Answer: _____ 6-packs

   Number model: 276 ÷ 6 = _____

2. We have tables that each seat 4 people. How many tables are needed to seat 178 people?

   10 [4s] = _____

   20 [4s] = _____

   30 [4s] = _____

   40 [4s] = _____

   50 [4s] = _____

   Answer: _____ tables

   Number model: _____ ÷ _____ → _____

3. How many 8s are there in 248?

   10 [8s] = _____

   20 [8s] = _____

   30 [8s] = _____

   40 [8s] = _____

   50 [8s] = _____

   Answer: _____

   Number model: 248 ÷ 8 = _____

4. How many 9s in 431?

   10 [9s] = _____

   20 [9s] = _____

   30 [9s] = _____

   40 [9s] = _____

   50 [9s] = _____

   Answer: _____

   Number model:  )‾‾‾‾‾

5. John is 245 days older than Alice. How many weeks older is John?

   Answer: _____
            weeks

   Number model:   7)245

6. The preschool held a tricycle parade. Trent counted 72 wheels. How many tricycles is that?

   Answer: _____
            tricycles

   Number model:  )‾‾‾‾‾

# Multiples of 10, 100, and 1,000

**1.**

How many [3s] are in 1,500? _____

_____ * 3 = 1,500

1,500 ÷ 3 = _____

**2.**

How many [40s] are in 2,800? _____

_____ * 40 = 2,800

2,800 ÷ 40 = _____

**3.** How many [8s] are in 720? _____

8 * _____ = 720

720 ÷ 8 = _____

**4.** How many [90s] are in 8,100? _____

90 * _____ = 8,100

8,100 ÷ 90 = _____

**5.** How many [70s] are in 350? _____

_____ * 70 = 350

350 ÷ 70 = _____

**6.** How many [800s] are in 3,200? _____

800 * _____ = 3,200

3,200 ÷ 800 = _____

**7.** How many [60s] are in 24,000? _____

_____ * 60 = 24,000

24,000 ÷ 60 = _____

**8.** How many [700s] are in 49,000? _____

700 * _____ = 49,000

49,000 ÷ 700 = _____

**9.** How many [30s] are in 18,000? _____

30 * _____ = 18,000

18,000 ÷ 30 = _____

**10.** How many [5s] are in 45,000? _____

_____ * 5 = 45,000

45,000 ÷ 5 = _____

**11.** How many [6,000s] are in 48,000? _____

6,000 * _____ = 48,000

48,000 ÷ 6,000 = _____

**12.** How many [700s] are in 56,000? _____

_____ * 700 = 56,000

56,000 ÷ 700 = _____

Use with Lesson 6.1.

## Math Boxes 6.1

**1.** Circle $\frac{1}{2}$ of the squares.

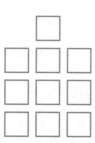

SRB
42

**2.** Solve each open sentence.

    **a.** $67 = A + (9 * 7)$     $A =$ _____

    **b.** $54 / 6 = 81 / B$       $B =$ _____

    **c.** $(C + 4) / 3 = 11$     $C =$ _____

    **d.** $(5 * D) / 4 = 10$     $D =$ _____

SRB
128 134

**3.** Round to the nearest thousand.

    **a.** 36,892     _____

    **b.** 3,245     _____

    **c.** 92,567     _____

    **d.** 105,833     _____

SRB
156 157

**4.** Multiply. Use the partial-products method.

    _____ $= 18 * 26$

SRB
17

**5.** Measure each line segment to the nearest millimeter.

    **a.** _____ _____ cm _____ mm
        P                                               S

    **b.** _____ _____ cm _____ mm
        A                               B

SRB
108

# Using the Partial-Quotients Division Algorithm

| These notations for division are equivalent: |
|:---:|
| $12\overline{)246}$       $246 \div 12$       $246 / 12$       $\dfrac{246}{12}$ |

Here is a division method you learned in class for dividing 185 by 8.

```
  8)185
  - 80  | 10        How many 8s are in 185? At least 10.
  -----            Use 10 as the first partial quotient. 10 * 8 = 80
   105             Subtract. At least 10 [8s] are left.
  - 80  | 10        Use 10 as the second partial quotient. 10 * 8 = 80
  -----            Subtract. At least 3 [8s] are left.
    25
  - 24  | 3         Use 3 as the third partial quotient. 3 * 8 = 24
  -----            Subtract. Add the partial quotients. 10 + 10 + 3 = 23
     1   23
```
    ↑     ↑
**Remainder  Quotient    Answer: 23 R1**

Divide.

1.  $4\overline{)96}$     Answer: _____

2.  $147 \div 9$     Answer: _____

3.  253 / 11     Answer: _____

4.  There are 184 plants to be put into pots.
    Each pot must contain 8 plants.
    How many pots are needed?

    Answer: _____ pots

    Number model: _____ ÷ _____ = _____

# Using the Partial-Quotients Division Algorithm (cont.)

**5.** 14)462    Answer: _____

**6.** 331 ÷ 7    Answer: _____

**7.** Twelve shirts fit into a box. There are 372 shirts to be put into boxes. How many boxes are needed?

Answer: _____ boxes

Number model: _____ ÷ _____ = _____

**8.** There are _____ players in the league. (Write a number greater than 100.)

There are _____ players on each team. (Write a number between 3 and 9.)

How many teams can be made?

Answer: _____ teams

Number model: _____ ÷ _____ → _____

# Math Boxes 6.2

---

**1.** Circle the fractions equivalent to $\frac{1}{2}$.

$\frac{3}{4}$      $\frac{4}{8}$      $\frac{8}{9}$      $\frac{7}{14}$      $\frac{3}{5}$      $\frac{5}{10}$

SRB 49

---

**2.** Complete.

a. 670 cm = _____ m

b. 4,800 cm = _____ m

c. 916 cm = _____ m _____ cm

d. 18 m = _____ cm

SRB 109

---

**3.** Round 409,381,886 to the nearest

a. hundred. _____

b. ten-thousand. _____

c. ten-million. _____

d. hundred-million. _____

SRB 156 157

---

**4.** Multiply. Use the lattice method.

_____ = 86 ∗ 29

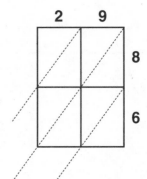

SRB 18

---

**5.** Add or subtract.

a. 0.64 + 1.73 = _____

b. 0.85 + 0.53 = _____

c. _____ = 3.05 − 0.67

d. 12.38 − 1.09 = _____

SRB 32-35

---

**6.** Divide.

490 ÷ 8    Answer: _____

SRB 21 22

---

Use with Lesson 6.2.

# Solving Multiplication and Division Number Stories

Fill in each Multiplication/Division Diagram. Estimate whether the answer will be in the tens, hundreds, or thousands. Then solve the problem and write a number model.

1. The profit from the book sale at Lincoln School was $725. The Math Club and four other clubs will share this amount equally. What will each club's share be?

| clubs | dollars per club | dollars in all |
|---|---|---|
|  |  |  |

**Estimate:** The answer will be in the   TENS   HUNDREDS   THOUSANDS.   (Circle one.)

**Answer:** _____

**Number model:** _____

2. The Box and Bin Store has 475 eight-ounce drinking glasses with "Happy Birthday" on them. These will be packed in boxes of 6, which will sell for $10.98 per box. How many packed boxes will there be?

| boxes | glasses per box | glasses in all |
|---|---|---|
|  |  |  |

**Estimate:** The answer will be in the   TENS   HUNDREDS   THOUSANDS.   (Circle one.)

**Answer:** _____

**Number model:** _____

3. Mr. Day lives 11 miles from his office. Last week he made 16 one-way trips between his home and office. How many miles did he drive in all?

| trips | miles per trip | miles in all |
|---|---|---|
|  |  |  |

**Estimate:** The answer will be in the   TENS   HUNDREDS   THOUSANDS.   (Circle one.)

**Answer:** _____

**Number model:** _____

# Solving Multiplication and Division Number Stories (cont.)

Fill in the Multiplication/Division Diagram. Estimate whether the answer will be in the tens, hundreds, or thousands. Then solve the problem and write a number model.

4. Martina and 3 friends sold 636 boxes of cookies for their club. Each girl sold the same number of boxes. How many boxes of cookies did each girl sell?

| girls | boxes per girl | boxes in all |
|-------|----------------|--------------|
|       |                |              |

**Estimate:** The answer will be in the   TENS   HUNDREDS   THOUSANDS.   (Circle one.)

**Answer:** _____

**Number model:** _____

Fill in both rows of the Multiplication/Division Diagram. Estimate whether the answer will be in the tens, hundreds, or thousands. Then solve the problem and write a number model.

5. The third and fourth grades received new science books. Eighteen boxes were delivered. Each box contained 12 books. How many books were received?

|  |  |  |
|--|--|--|
|  |  |  |

**Estimate:** The answer will be in the   TENS   HUNDREDS   THOUSANDS.   (Circle one.)

**Answer:** _____

**Number model:** _____

Use with Lesson 6.3.

# Math Boxes 6.3

**1.** Circle $\frac{5}{6}$ of the squares.

**2.** Solve each open sentence.

  a. $79 = A + (8 * 9)$    $A =$ _____

  b. $48 / 6 = 40 / B$    $B =$ _____

  c. $(C + 8) / 4 = 7$    $C =$ _____

  d. $(6 * D) / 3 = 12$    $D =$ _____

**3.** Round each to the nearest ten-thousand.

  a. 150,983    _____

  b. 786,042    _____

  c. 12,903,899    _____

  d. 79,067,409    _____

**4.** Multiply. Use the partial-products method.

$54 * 93 =$ _____

**5.** Measure each line segment to the nearest millimeter.

  a. _____
  R                                                S

  _____ cm _____ mm

  b. _____
  C                                     S

  _____ cm _____ mm

# Rewriting and Interpreting Remainders

> **Example** 169 ÷ 5 → 33 R4
>
> The remainder R4 can be written as $\frac{4}{5}$.
>
> The answer 33 R4 can be written as $33\frac{4}{5}$.
>
> The answer can also be written as a decimal. $33\frac{4}{5} = 33.8$

Write each answer as a mixed number by rewriting the remainder as a fraction.

1. $\overset{13 \text{ R1}}{2\overline{)27}}$

2. $\overset{88 \text{ R3}}{10\overline{)883}}$

3. $\overset{15 \text{ R12}}{16\overline{)252}}$

4. $\overset{7 \text{ R70}}{100\overline{)770}}$

_____      _____      _____      _____

Divide, rewrite the remainder as fraction or decimal, and keep the fraction or decimal as part of the final answer.

5. A board 93 inches long is cut into 12 pieces of equal length. How long is each piece?

_____ inches

6. It costs $50 to buy 8 adult tickets to the school play. What is the cost per ticket?

$ _____

Solve. Be prepared to tell what you did when there was a remainder—ignored it, made it part of the answer, or rounded up the answer.

7. The school library is buying boxes to store 128 videotapes. Each box holds 6 tapes. How many boxes are needed to store all of the tapes?

_____ boxes

8. Jackson is having a party. Balloons cost $6 per bunch. How many bunches can he buy with $75?

_____ bunches

9. There are 196 note cards. They are shared equally by 14 students. How many note cards does each student get?

_____ note cards

10. Eight $\frac{1}{2}$-hour guitar lessons cost $60. What is the cost per lesson?

$ _____

# Writing Multiplication and Division Number Stories

The following number models can be used to help solve number stories. For each, write a number story. Then ask your partner to solve it and write the solution, including any units. At the same time, solve your partner's story.

**1.** $4 * 36 = ?$

**Number story:** _____

_____

_____

_____

**Solution:** _____

(unit)

**2.** $8)\overline{360} = ?$

**Number story:** _____

_____

_____

_____

**Solution:** _____

(unit)

**3.** $5,280 / 6 = ?$

**Number story:** _____

_____

_____

_____

**Solution:** _____

(unit)

# Math Boxes 6.4

**1.** Circle the fractions equivalent to $\frac{1}{2}$.

$\frac{8}{16}$    $\frac{5}{6}$    $\frac{6}{12}$    $\frac{2}{3}$    $\frac{12}{24}$    $\frac{8}{15}$

**2.** Complete.

a. 320 cm = _____ m

b. 5,600 cm = _____ m

c. 412 cm = _____ m _____ cm

d. 12 m = _____ cm

**3.** Round 5,906,245 to the nearest

a. million.        _____

b. ten-thousand.  _____

c. thousand.      _____

d. hundred.       _____

**4.** Multiply. Use the lattice method.

_____ = 58 * 52

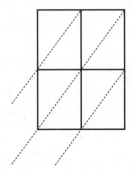

**5.** Add or subtract.

a. 2.01 + 5.01 = _____

b. 0.37 + 0.26 = _____

c. _____ = 7.80 − 3.65

d. 6.79 − 6.55 = _____

**6.** Divide.

872 ÷ 5    Answer: _____

Use with Lesson 6.4.

Date _____                    Time _____

# A Map of the Island of Ireland

| Bantry | B–1 | Dublin | F–4 | Lahinch | B–4 | Omagh | E–7 |
|--------|-----|--------|-----|---------|-----|-------|-----|
| Belfast | F–7 | Dundalk | F–6 | Larne | F–7 | Tralee | B–2 |
| Carlow | E–3 | Galway | C–4 | Limerick | C–3 | Tuam | C–5 |
| Castlebar | B–6 | Gort | C–4 | Mullingar | E–5 | Westport | B–5 |
| Derry | E–8 | Kilkee | B–3 | Navan | E–5 | Wicklow | F–4 |

# A Campground Map

SCALE

0    0.2    0.4    0.6    0.8    1 km

N
W    E
S

County Road

Parking Lot

Camping Area

Blue Lake

Picnic Area

Fishing Dock

Lake Trail

Gravel Road

Canoe
Rental

Ranger Station
and House

Paved Road          Trail          Camping Area

Unpaved Road          River          Picnic Area

# Finding Distances on a Map

Use the campground map on journal page 160 to complete the following:

1. Suppose you hiked along the lake trail from the fishing dock to the parking lot. Estimate the distance you hiked.                    About _____ km

2. The ranger made her hourly check. She started at the ranger station. She drove northwest and then north on Gravel Road to County Road. She turned east onto County Road and drove past the parking lot and the camping area. After she passed the canoe rental, she turned right onto Gravel Road and drove back to the ranger station. About what distance did she drive?                    About _____ km

3. Estimate the distance around Blue Lake.                    About _____ km

4. You are planning to hike from the camping area to the parking lot. You will stay on the roads or trails. You want to hike at least 5 kilometers.

   a. Plan your route. Then draw it on the map with a coloring pencil or crayon.

   b. Estimate the distance.                    About _____ km

5. Use the ordered number pairs to locate each item on the map. Mark a dot at the location. Next to the dot, write the letter given for the item.

### Campground Features Chart

|  | Location | Letter |
|---|---|---|
| parked car | (5,9) | C |
| boat | $(3\frac{1}{2},8)$ | B |
| swing set | (8,11) | S |
| hikers | (10.5,6.5) | H |
| farmhouse | $(\frac{1}{2},7)$ | F |

# Rewriting Remainders

Write each answer as a mixed number by rewriting the remainder as a fraction.

1. $2\overline{)79}$   39 R1

2. $10\overline{)446}$   44 R6

3. $8\overline{)394}$   49 R2

4. $16\overline{)860}$   53 R12

_____        _____        _____        _____

Divide. Write each answer as a mixed number by writing the remainder as a fraction.

5. $427 \div 2$     **Answer:** _____

6. $390 / 9$     **Answer:** _____

7. $12\overline{)675}$     **Answer:** _____

# Math Boxes 6.5

**1. a.** Shade $\frac{1}{2}$ of the square.

**b.** Shade $\frac{2}{3}$ of the square.

SRB
42

**2.** Complete.

**a.** 350 cm = _____ m

**b.** 1,500 cm = _____ m

**c.** 458 cm = _____ m _____ cm

**d.** 9 m = _____ cm

**e.** 3.2 m = _____ cm

SRB
109 259

**3.** The Sports Boosters raised $908 at their annual chili supper. The money will be shared equally by 4 athletic teams. How much money will each team receive?

_____

SRB
21 22

**4.** Multiply. Use the partial-products method.

66 * 62 = _____

SRB
17

**5.** Insert parentheses to make each number sentence true.

**a.** 15 + 5 * 6 = 120

**b.** 7 + 9 * 2 = 25

**c.** 77 = 1 + 6 * 6 + 5

SRB
129

**6.** Draw a line segment that is 2 inches long. Mark the following inch measurements on the line segment: $\frac{3}{4}$, $\frac{7}{8}$, $1\frac{1}{8}$, and $1\frac{1}{2}$.

SRB
108

# Making an Angle Measurer

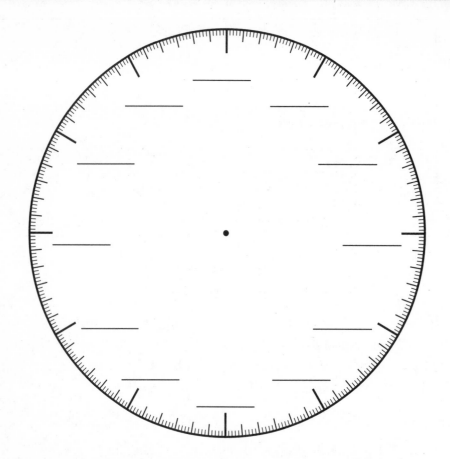

There are 360 marks around the circle. They divide the edge of the circle into 360 small spaces. Twelve of the marks are longer than the rest. They are in the same positions as the 12 numbers around a clock face. Your teacher will tell you how to label the 12 large marks on the circle.

## The Babylonian Number System

The Babylonians lived about 3,000 years ago in what is now the country of Iraq. Babylon was on the Euphrates River. It was not far from Baghdad, which is the current capital of Iraq.

The Babylonians used a numbering system based on the number 60. Today, Babylonian ideas are used to measure time. The hour is divided into 60 minutes, and the minute into 60 seconds.

The number 60 is also used in measuring angles. A full turn measures 360°, and 360° is a multiple of 60° (6 * 60° = 360°).

# Clock Angles

1. How many minutes does the minute hand move

   a. from 12:00 to 12:30? _____     b. from 1:00 to 1:15? _____

2. How many degrees does the minute hand move

   a. from 12:00 to 12:30? _____     b. from 1:00 to 1:15? _____

   c. from 2:00 to 2:05?   _____     d. from 5:00 to 5:01? _____

3. How many degrees does the hour hand move

   a. in 1 hour?          _____

   b. in $\frac{1}{2}$ an hour?       _____

   c. in 10 minutes?     _____

## Challenge

4. How long does it take the hour hand to move 1°?          _____
   (*Hint:* How many degrees does it move in 10 minutes?)

5. How long does it take the minute hand to move 1°?        _____
   (*Hint:* How many degrees does it move in 1 minute?)

# Math Boxes 6.6

**1.** For this spinner, what color would you be *most likely* to land on?

_____

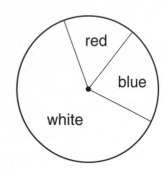

red

blue

white

SRB
70 72

**2.** Multiply. Use the lattice method.

_____ = 19 * 473

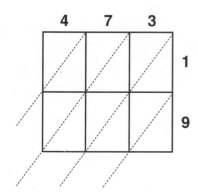

4   7   3

1

9

SRB
18

**3.** Plot and label each point on the coordinate grid.

SRB
124

A (0,4)

B (1,0)

C (5,2)

D (2,2)

E (3,1)

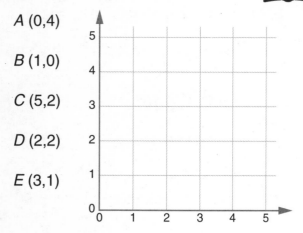

**4.** Divide. Write the remainder as a fraction.

SRB
21 22
153

883 / 7 = _____

**5.** Write >, <, or = to make each number sentence true.

a.  65,000,000 _____ 92,000,000

b.  four hundred thousand _____ $10^4$

c.  $10^2$ _____ 1,000

SRB
6 128

**6.** Juan talked on the phone an average of 34 minutes per week for 1 whole year. About how many minutes did Juan spend on the phone in 1 year?

_____ minutes

Use with Lesson 6.6.

# Measuring Angles with a 360° Angle Measurer

Use your angle measurer to measure each angle.

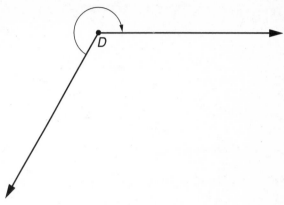

**1.** ∠C measures _____°.

**2.** ∠D measures _____°.

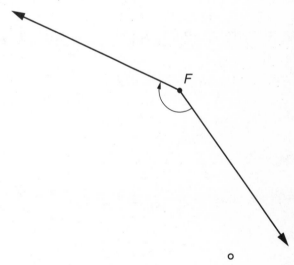

**3.** ∠E measures _____°.

**4.** ∠F measures _____°.

# Coordinate Grids

1. Plot and label each point on the coordinate grid.

| | |
|---|---|
| A | (1,7) |
| B | (6,6) |
| C | (10,1) |
| D | (4,3) |
| E | (8,6) |
| F | (2,9) |
| G | (9,1) |
| H | (10,4) |

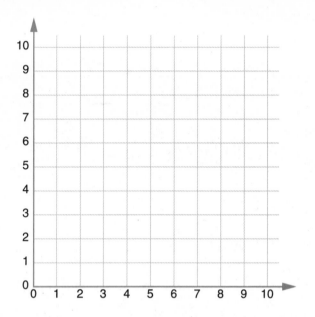

2. Write the ordered number pair for each point plotted on the coordinate grid.

I ( _____ , _____ )

J ( _____ , _____ )

K ( _____ , _____ )

L ( _____ , _____ )

M ( _____ , _____ )

N ( _____ , _____ )

O ( _____ , _____ )

P ( _____ , _____ )

Q ( _____ , _____ )

R ( _____ , _____ )

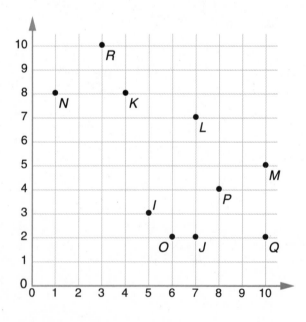

Use with Lesson 6.7.

# Math Boxes 6.7

---

**1. a.** Shade $\frac{1}{3}$ of the rectangle.

**b.** Shade $\frac{3}{4}$ of the rectangle.

---

**2.** Complete.

**a.** 750 cm = _____ m

**b.** 3,500 cm = _____ m

**c.** 797 cm = _____ m _____ cm

**d.** 8 m = _____ cm

**e.** 9.7 m = _____ cm

---

**3.** 27 fourth grade students collected newspapers for one week. If they collected a total of 2,078 newspapers by the end of the week, on average about how many papers did each student collect?

_____ newspapers

---

**4.** Multiply. Use the partial-products method.

67 * 34 = _____

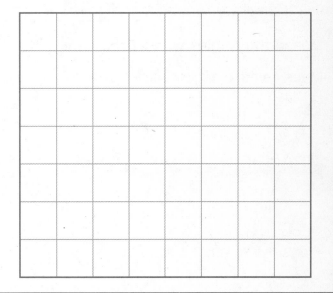

---

**5.** Insert parentheses to make each number sentence true.

**a.** 66 − 16 * 4 = 200

**b.** 49 = 4 + 3 * 42 / 6

**c.** 12 = 15 − 2 + 1

---

**6.** Draw a line segment that is $1\frac{3}{4}$ inches long. Mark the following inch measurements on the line segment: $\frac{1}{4}$, $\frac{5}{8}$, $1\frac{3}{8}$, and $1\frac{1}{2}$.

---

# Drawing and Measuring Angles

## Math Message

Use a straightedge to draw the following angles. Do **not** use an angle measurer.

∠A: any angle
less than 90°

∠B: any angle more than
90° and less than 180°

∠C: any angle more
than 180°

∠A is called an
**acute angle.**

∠B is called an
**obtuse angle.**

∠C is called a
**reflex angle.**

## Measuring Angles with a Protractor

Measure each angle as accurately as you can.

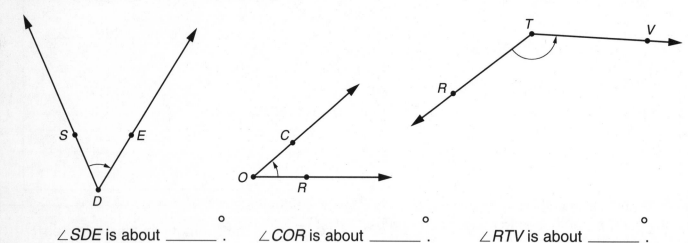

∠SDE is about _____°.

∠COR is about _____°.

∠RTV is about _____°.

| Date | Time |

# Exploring Triangle Measures

Work with a partner. You will each need a sheet of paper, a straightedge, and a protractor.

1. Each partner draws a large triangle on a separate sheet of paper. The two triangles should not look the same.

2. Label the vertices of one triangle *A, B,* and *C.* Label the vertices of the other triangle *D, E,* and *F.*

3. Use your protractors to measure each angle as accurately as you can.

4. Record the degree measures in the tables below.

5. Find the sum of the degree measures of triangle *ABC* and triangle *DEF.*

| Angle | Degree Measure |
|---|---|
| ∠A | About _____° |
| ∠B | About _____° |
| ∠C | About _____° |
| Sum | About _____° |

| Angle | Degree Measure |
|---|---|
| ∠D | About _____° |
| ∠E | About _____° |
| ∠F | About _____° |
| Sum | About _____° |

6. Write a true statement about the three angles of a triangle.

_____

_____

_____

Date _____    Time _____

**1.** Fill in the missing fractions on the number line.

0                                    1

_____   _____   _____

**2.** Round to the nearest hundred-thousand.

a. 37,609,034 _____

b. 9,540,234 _____

c. 290,696,332 _____

d. 78,291,554 _____

SRB 156 157

**3.** Measure angle *EDF.*

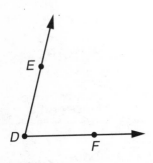

E

D       F

°

measure of ∠*EDF* = _____ .

∠*EDF* is _____ (acute or obtuse).

SRB 78 79

SRB 12-123

**4.** Divide. Write the remainder as a fraction.

SRB 21 22 153

_____ = 482 / 7

**5.** Name the ordered number pair for each point plotted on the coordinate grid.

A (___ , ___)

B (___ , ___)

C (___ , ___)

D (___ , ___)

E (___ , ___)

SRB 124

**6.** Complete the "What's My Rule?" table and state the rule.

| Rule | in | out |
|------|-----|-----|
|      | 3.6 | 2.1 |
|      | 10  | 8.5 |
|      | 7.2 |     |
|      |     | 4.9 |

SRB 142-146

172

Use with Lesson 6.8.

# Drawing Angles

1. Draw a 15° angle, using
   ray *AB* as one of its sides.

A                                    B

2. Draw a 150° angle, using
   ray *CD* as one of its sides.

D                              C

3. Draw a 60° angle, using
   ray *EF* as one of its sides.

F                              E

4. Draw a 35° angle, using
   segment *GH* as one of its
   sides.

G                                              H

5. Draw a 330° angle, using
   ray *IJ* as one of its sides.

I                              J

# Math Boxes 6.9

**1.** For this spinner, which color would you be *least likely* to land on?

_____

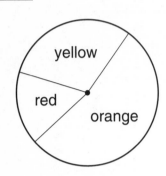

**2.** Multiply. Use the lattice method.

_____ = 18 * 240

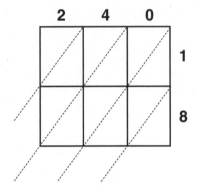

**3.** Plot and label each point on the coordinate grid.

A (0,3)

B (3,0)

C (3,2)

D (4,4)

E (5,1)

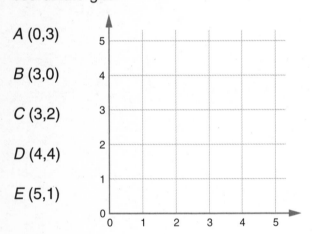

**4.** Divide. Write the remainder as a fraction.

598 / 3 = _____

**5.** Write >, <, or = to make each number sentence true.

a. 33,000,000 _____ 33 million

b. six hundred thousand _____ $10^6$

c. $10^4$ _____ 10,000

d. 5,200,000 _____ 9 billion

**6.** During a classroom clean-up of the school, each student is to pick up at least 15 pieces of garbage. Mrs. Baker's class has 27 students. What is the least number of pieces of garbage they should pick up?

_____ pieces

Date _____                                    Time _____

# Locating Places on Regional Maps

1. Find each of the following cities on the maps in the World Tour section of your
   *Student Reference Book.* Record the continent in which it is located.

   a. Lisbon, Portugal          _____
      (on Region 2 map)

   b. Mumbai (Bombay), India    _____
      (on Region 4 map)

   c. La Paz, Bolivia           _____
      (on Region 3 map)

   d. Pretoria, South Africa    _____

   e. Vancouver, Canada         _____

2. Use the maps of continents to find the approximate latitude and longitude of each city.

   a. Lisbon, Portugal    latitude _____ ° *North* ; longitude _____ ° *West*

   b. Mumbai, India       latitude _____ ° _____ ; longitude _____ ° _____

   c. La Paz, Bolivia     latitude _____ ° _____ ; longitude _____ ° _____

   d. Pretoria, S. Africa latitude _____ ° _____ ; longitude _____ ° _____

   e. Vancouver, Canada   latitude _____ ° _____ ; longitude _____ ° _____

3. Each degree of latitude (traveling north or south from the equator) is equal to
   about 70 miles. About how many miles from the equator is each city listed below?

   a. Lisbon, Portugal          About _____ miles

   b. Mumbai, India             About _____ miles

   c. La Paz, Bolivia           About _____ miles

   d. Pretoria, South Africa    About _____ miles

   e. Vancouver, Canada         About _____ miles

Use with Lesson 6.10.                                                  **175**

**1.** Fill in the missing fractions on the number line.

_____  _____  _____  _____

**2.** Round to the nearest thousand.

a. 8,289,500 _____

b. 725,311 _____

c. 451,062 _____

d. 12,000,852 _____

**3.** Measure angle *NMO*.

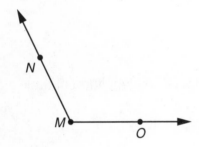

measure of ∠*NMO* = _____

∠*NMO* is _____ (acute or obtuse).

**4.** Divide. Write the remainder as a fraction.

_____ = 497 / 3

**5.** Name the ordered number pair for each point plotted on the coordinate grid.

*A* (____ , ____)

*B* (____ , ____)

*C* (____ , ____)

*D* (____ , ____)

*E* (____ , ____)

**6.** Complete the "What's My Rule?" table and state the rule.

| Rule | in | out |
|------|------|------|
|      | 3.66 | 7.04 |
|      | 0.42 | 3.80 |
|      | 8.73 |      |
|      |      | 12.66 |

## Time to Reflect

1. Do you think division is easy or hard? Explain your answer.

_____

_____

_____

_____

2. Write 5 sentences that each contain the word *angle*. At least 2 of the sentences must be about mathematics.

   a. _____

   _____

   b. _____

   _____

   c. _____

   _____

   d. _____

   _____

   e. _____

   _____

3. After working in this unit, do you find it easier to find places on a globe? Why or why not?

_____

_____

_____

Use with Lesson 6.11.

Date

Time

## Math Boxes 6.11

**1.** Fill in the missing fractions on the number lines.

**a.**

$1\frac{2}{5}$ ___ ___ ___ ___ $2\frac{2}{5}$

**b.**

$2\frac{1}{2}$ ___ ___ ___ ___ 5

**2.** Draw 12 balloons. Circle $\frac{5}{12}$ of the balloons. Mark X on $\frac{1}{4}$ of the balloons.

**3.** Write five names for $\frac{1}{4}$.

_____

_____

_____

_____

_____

**4. a.** Shade $\frac{5}{6}$ of the hexagon.

**b.** Shade $\frac{2}{3}$ of the hexagon.

**5.** Design a spinner such that it is more likely that you will land on red than on green.

**178**

Use with Lesson 6.11.

# My Route Log

| Date | Country | Capital | Air distance from last capital | Total distance traveled so far |
|------|---------|---------|-------------------------------|-------------------------------|
|  | 1 U.S.A. | Washington, D.C. | ███████ |  |
|  | 2 Egypt | Cairo |  |  |
|  | 3 |  |  |  |
|  | 4 |  |  |  |
|  | 5 |  |  |  |
|  | 6 |  |  |  |
|  | 7 |  |  |  |
|  | 8 |  |  |  |
|  | 9 |  |  |  |
|  | 10 |  |  |  |
|  | 11 |  |  |  |
|  | 12 |  |  |  |
|  | 13 |  |  |  |
|  | 14 |  |  |  |
|  | 15 |  |  |  |
|  | 16 |  |  |  |
|  | 17 |  |  |  |
|  | 18 |  |  |  |
|  | 19 |  |  |  |
|  | 20 |  |  |  |

Use with Lesson 3.5.

# Route Map

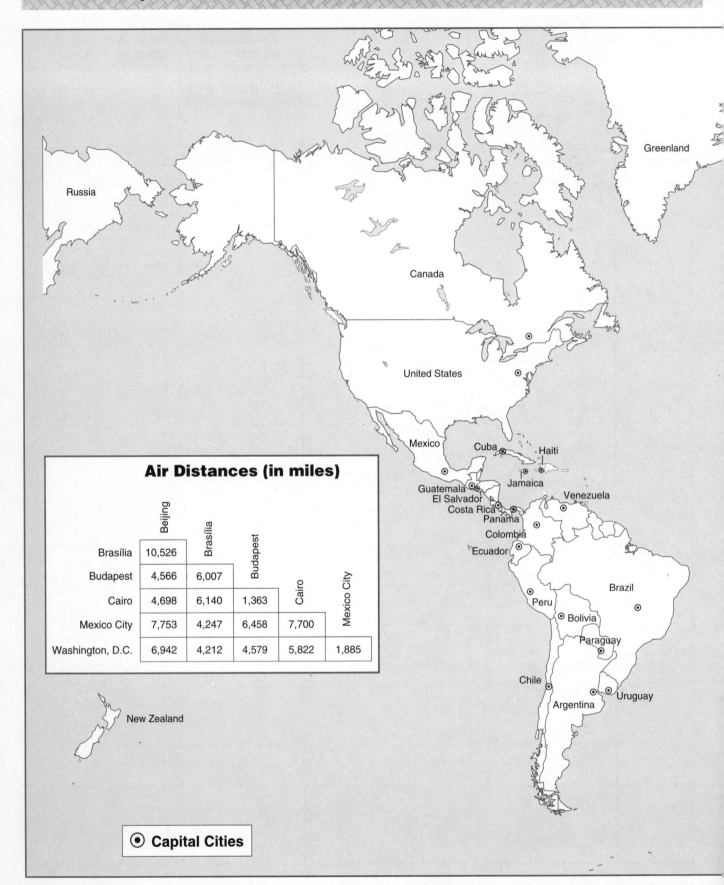

**Air Distances (in miles)**

| | Beijing | Brasília | Budapest | Cairo | Mexico City |
|---|---|---|---|---|---|
| Brasília | 10,526 | | | | |
| Budapest | 4,566 | 6,007 | | | |
| Cairo | 4,698 | 6,140 | 1,363 | | |
| Mexico City | 7,753 | 4,247 | 6,458 | 7,700 | |
| Washington, D.C. | 6,942 | 4,212 | 4,579 | 5,822 | 1,885 |

⊙ **Capital Cities**

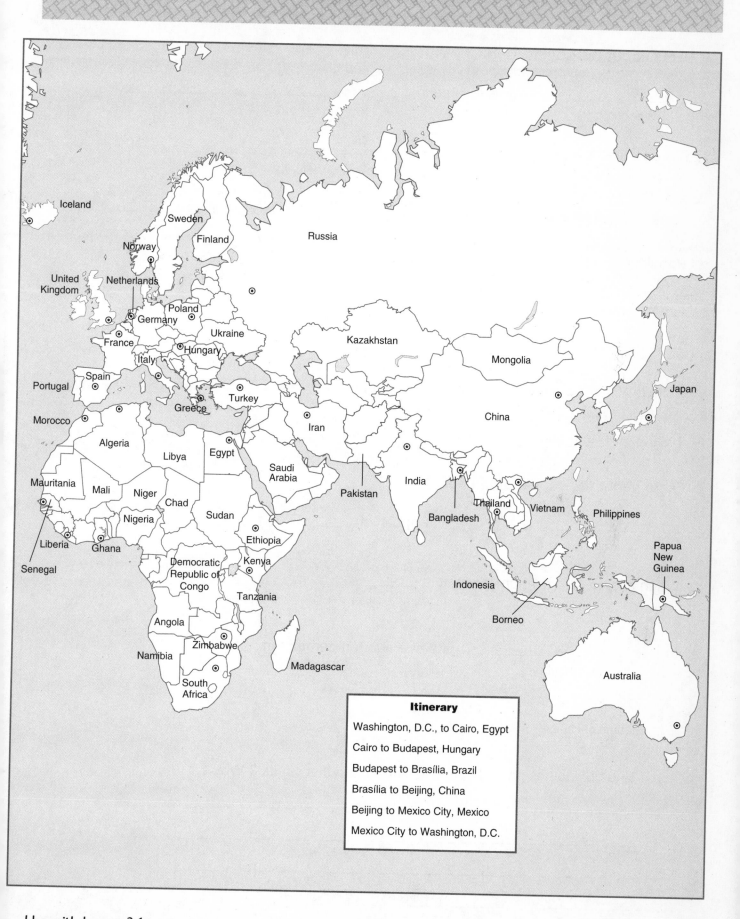

Iceland

Sweden

Norway     Finland

United
Kingdom    Netherlands

Russia

Poland

Germany

Ukraine

France

Hungary

Italy

Spain

Portugal

Greece

Turkey

Kazakhstan

Mongolia

Japan

Morocco

Iran

China

Algeria

Egypt

Libya

Saudi
Arabia

Mauritania

Mali

Niger

Chad

Pakistan

India

Nigeria

Sudan

Thailand

Vietnam

Philippines

Liberia

Ghana

Ethiopia

Bangladesh

Senegal

Democratic
Republic of
Congo

Kenya

Tanzania

Papua
New
Guinea

Angola

Indonesia

Namibia

Zimbabwe

Borneo

South
Africa

Madagascar

Australia

**Itinerary**

Washington, D.C., to Cairo, Egypt

Cairo to Budapest, Hungary

Budapest to Brasília, Brazil

Brasília to Beijing, China

Beijing to Mexico City, Mexico

Mexico City to Washington, D.C.

Use with Lesson 2.1.

# My Country Notes

## A. Facts about the country

_____ is located in _____.
    name of country                                      name of continent

1. It is bordered by _____
                                countries, bodies of water

_____.

2. Population: _____    Area: _____ square miles

3. Languages spoken: _____

_____

4. Monetary unit: _____

5. Exchange rate (optional): 1 _____ = _____

## B. Facts about the capital of the country

_____          Population: _____
    name of capital

1. When it is noon in my hometown, it is _____ in _____.
                                     time (A.M. or P.M.?)    name of capital

2. In _____, the average temperature in
             month

_____ is about _____ °F.
    name of capital

3. What kinds of clothes should I pack for my visit to this capital? Why?

_____

_____

_____

_____

# My Country Notes (cont.)

4. Turn to the Route Map found on journal pages 180 and 181.
   Draw a line from the last city you visited to the capital of this country.

5. If your class is using the Route Log, take journal page 179 or *Math Masters,* page
   38 and record the information.

6. Can you find any facts on pages 246–249 in your *Student Reference Book* that
   apply to this country? For example, is one of the 10 tallest mountains in the world
   located in this country? List all the facts you can find.

   _____

   _____

   _____

   _____

   _____

## c. My impressions about the country

   Do you know anyone who has visited or lived in this country? If so, ask
   that person for an interview. Read about the country's customs and about
   interesting places to visit there. Use encyclopedias, travel books, the travel section
   of a newspaper, or library books. Try to get brochures from a travel agent. Then
   describe below some interesting things you have learned about this country.

   _____

   _____

   _____

   _____

   _____

   _____

   _____

   _____

   _____

## My Country Notes

### A. Facts about the country

_____ is located in _____.
name of country                          name of continent

1. It is bordered by _____
                            countries, bodies of water

_____.

2. Population: _____     Area: _____ square miles

3. Languages spoken: _____

_____

4. Monetary unit: _____

5. Exchange rate (optional): 1 _____ = _____

### B. Facts about the capital of the country

_____     Population: _____
name of capital

1. When it is noon in my hometown, it is _____ in _____.
                                              time (A.M. or P.M.?)     name of capital

2. In _____, the average temperature in
      month

_____ is about _____ °F.
name of capital

3. What kinds of clothes should I pack for my visit to this capital? Why?

_____

_____

_____

_____

## My Country Notes (cont.)

4. Turn to the Route Map found on journal pages 180 and 181.
   Draw a line from the last city you visited to the capital of this country.

5. If your class is using the Route Log, take journal page 179 or *Math Masters,* page 38 and record the information.

6. Can you find any facts on pages 246–249 in your *Student Reference Book* that apply to this country? For example, is one of the 10 tallest mountains in the world located in this country? List all the facts you can find.

_____

_____

_____

_____

_____

**c. My impressions about the country**

Do you know anyone who has visited or lived in this country? If so, ask that person for an interview. Read about the country's customs and about interesting places to visit there. Use encyclopedias, travel books, the travel section of a newspaper, or library books. Try to get brochures from a travel agent. Then describe below some interesting things you have learned about this country.

_____

_____

_____

_____

_____

_____

_____

_____

_____

## My Country Notes

### A. Facts about the country

_____ is located in _____.
    name of country                                              name of continent

1. It is bordered by _____
                              countries, bodies of water

_____.

2. Population: _____      Area: _____ square miles

3. Languages spoken: _____

_____

4. Monetary unit: _____

5. Exchange rate (optional): 1 _____ = _____

### B. Facts about the capital of the country

_____ Population: _____
    name of capital

1. When it is noon in my hometown, it is _____ in _____.
                                     time (A.M. or P.M.?)      name of capital

2. In _____, the average temperature in
       month

_____ is about _____ °F.
  name of capital

3. What kinds of clothes should I pack for my visit to this capital? Why?

_____

_____

_____

_____

                          Use with Lesson 5.11.

# My Country Notes (cont.)

4. Turn to the Route Map found on journal pages 180 and 181.
   Draw a line from the last city you visited to the capital of this country.

5. If your class is using the Route Log, take journal page 179 or *Math Masters,* page
   38 and record the information.

6. Can you find any facts on pages 246–249 in your *Student Reference Book* that
   apply to this country? For example, is one of the 10 tallest mountains in the world
   located in this country? List all the facts you can find.

_____

_____

_____

_____

_____


c. **My impressions about the country**

Do you know anyone who has visited or lived in this country? If so, ask
that person for an interview. Read about the country's customs and about
interesting places to visit there. Use encyclopedias, travel books, the travel section
of a newspaper, or library books. Try to get brochures from a travel agent. Then
describe below some interesting things you have learned about this country.

_____

_____

_____

_____

_____

_____

_____

_____

_____

# *, / Fact Triangles 1

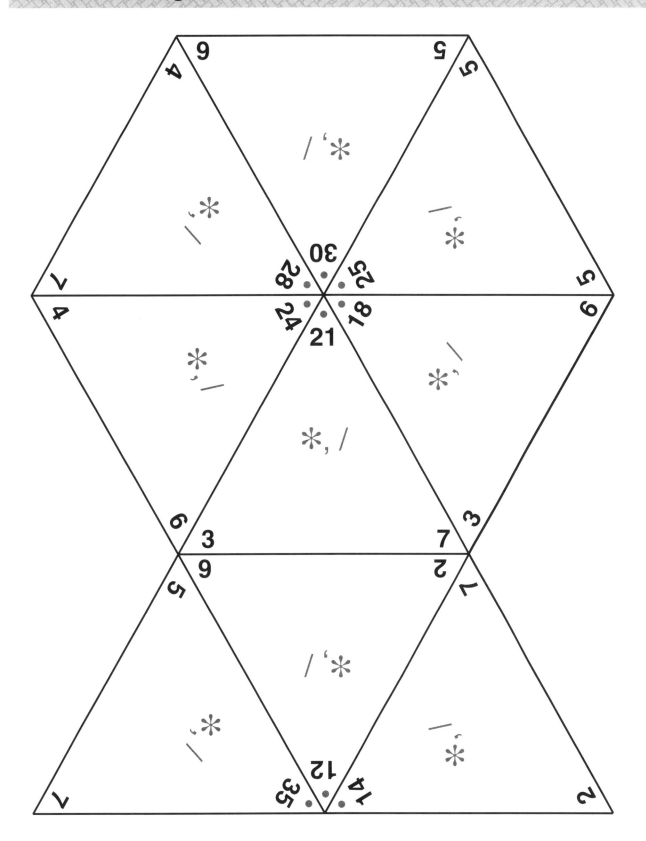

# *, / Fact Triangles 2

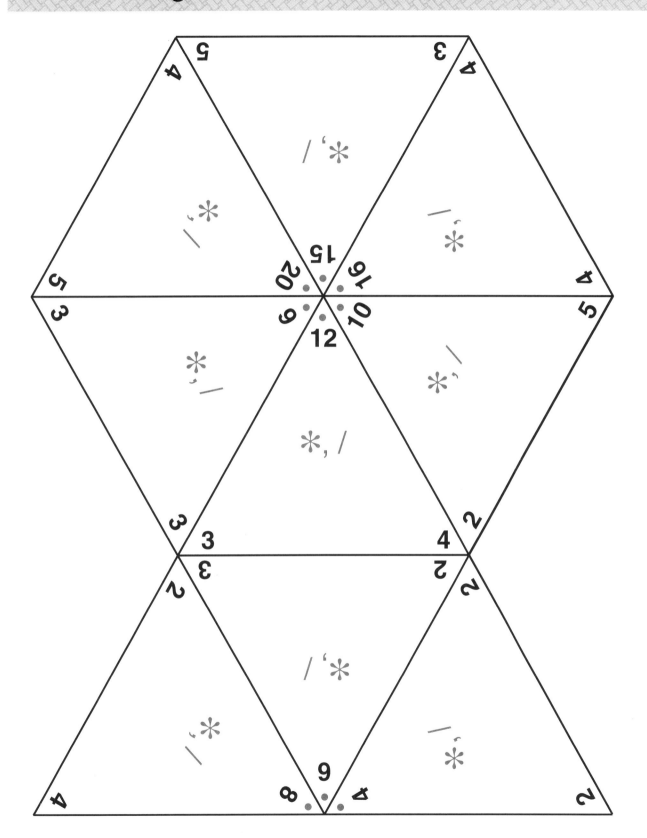

# *, / Fact Triangles 3

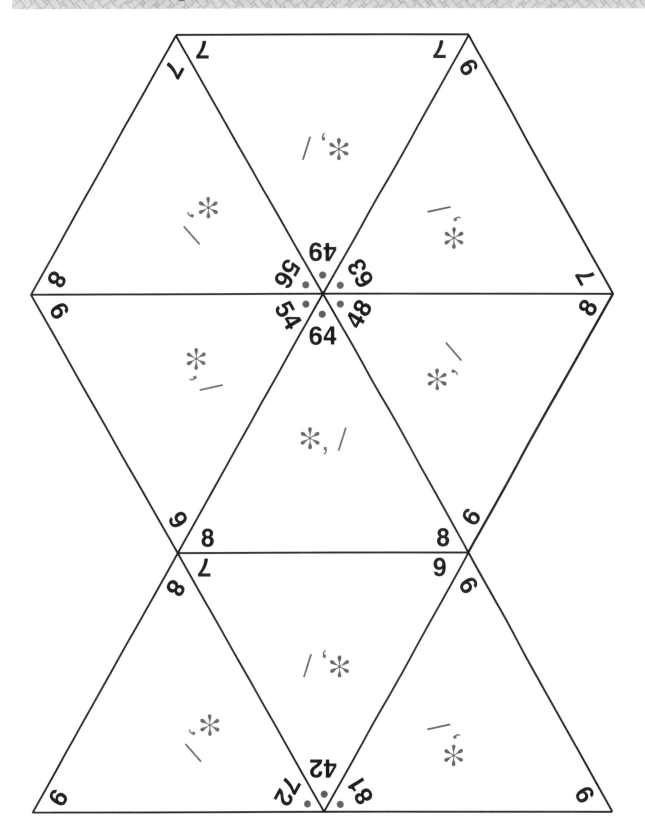

# *, / Fact Triangles 4

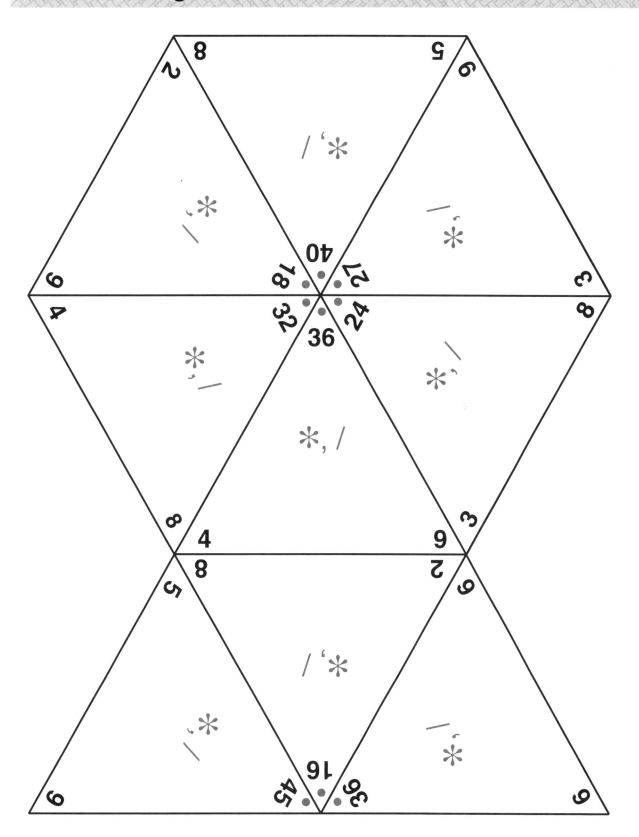